NIKOLA TESLA
The Life and Inventions
of a Genius

For the publisher
Bora Babić, director

ALEKSANDAR MARINČIĆ

NIKOLA TESLA

The Life and Inventions
of a Genius

AKADEMSKA KNJIGA
NOVI SAD

CONTENTS

VI GREAT INVENTIONS

I
CHILDHOOD AND EDUCATION

ORIGIN

Nikola Tesla and his ancestors came from an area known as *Military Frontier* or *Krajina*. The Military Frontier was established by the Habsburgs in the territory of Croatia and Slavonia in the 16th century, whilst Banat was incorporated in the 17th century. The establishment of the borderland was the result of a need to defend Austria from Turkish attacks, and also because of the wave of migrations from the Turkish territories. As early as the beginning of the 15th century, under the leadership of the Serb nobility, Serbs served as soldiers of the Military Frontier, as *šajkaši* who held positions on Panonia rivers. At the end of the same century, Turks gave some of the Serbs the status of *Vlachs*, and their leaders the status of landowners and princes, with the obligation to guard the border and provide troops for further conquests, as well as to pay a capitation tax or *harač* to the Sultan[1].

As countries on the borders of the Habsburg Monarchy were losing significant parts of the population due to Turkish incursions, Austrian authorities gladly accepted all migrants who were willing to abandon the Turkish border and enter the service of the neighboring country. The condition under which the Sultan's subjects accepted to move included recognition of the same privileges they enjoyed within the Turkish border. They were given autonomous government and exemption from feudal serfdom; military service remained as the only obligation to the monarchy. The majority of Vlachs settled in the Military Frontier at the beginning of the 16th and 17th centuries.

In peaceful times, the main activity of frontiersmen was cattle breeding. The "Vlach Statute," proclaimed by Austria in 1630, confirmed the privileges to the settlers, but imposed on them the obligation to wage war on other fronts of the Empire against France, Italy and Prussia. When the dual Austro-Hungarian Monarchy was proclaimed in 1867, the Military Frontier became an anachronism; it was demilitarized, and around 1873 abolished as a special territorial unit. Military service became compulsory at that time.

After the victory of Napoleon over Austria, and signing of the Schoenbrunn Peace Treaty in 1809, the Military Frontier and the largest part of Slovenia and Northern Croatia were ceded to France as Illyrian Provinces. The frontiersmen were loyal to the new rulers and many served in the French Army.

A six-year period of Napoleon's administration had a favorable impact on social development in these provinces. Reforms introduced by Napoleon – such as abolishment of serfdom, introduction of civic administration and judiciary in accordance with the French legislation, limitation of the temporal rights of the church, and introduction of education in mother tongue – accelerated the disintegration of surviving feudal institutions, although the economic situation of people was difficult. Napoleon's withdrawal from power after the defeat at Waterloo in 1815 was therefore welcomed.[2]

Soon after Napoleon's defeat, Nikola Tesla's grandfather, a frontiersman of the same name from the Raduč Village, married Ana Kalinić, the daughter of a famous officer. After the collapse of Illyria, Nikola senior moved to Gospić, where he had five children, among them a son, Milutin, who was born on February 3, 1819. Grandfather Nikola served as a sergeant in Napoleon's Army and was awarded a medal for distinguished conduct, making the whole family very proud. Hence his love for France, which he passed on to younger generations. Milutin's mother Ana, nee Kalinić, was also a child of a frontiersman. According to some accounts, Tesla's distant ancestors initially bore the surname of Draganić, while the surname Tesla was adopted later, from a nickname given to one of the ancestors because of his front teeth which looked like a carpenters axe –   (S   .[3]

Milutin Tesla attended a German secondary school in Gospić, and subsequently, on his father's insistence, enrolled in the Military Academy with his younger brother Josif. Milutin Tesla did not like the military career and decided to leave the Military Academy and become a priest. His brother was not enthusiastic about the military profession either and chose to take up the position of a mathematics teacher, first in Gospic, and then at the Austrian Military Academy.

Milutin Tesla entered Theological School in Plaško and graduated in 1845 as the best student. He married Djuka Mandić, a daughter of priest Nikola Mandić from Gračac, and sister of later Metropolitan Petar Mandić. Milutin took his first job as a pastor in Senj. During six years in Senj, Milutin and Djuka had three children, daughter Milka, son Dane and daughter Angelina. In 1852, Milutin was transferred to Smiljan as an administrator where their second son Nikola and third daughter Marica were born.

CHILDHOOD

During the night between the 9th and 10th of July 1856, in the village of Smiljan, Lika, Milutin and Djuka Tesla had their second son and fourth child. Who could have guessed at the time that a genius was born, a man who would transform the next century and fascinate the world with the beauty and importance of his achievements and ideas, more than half a

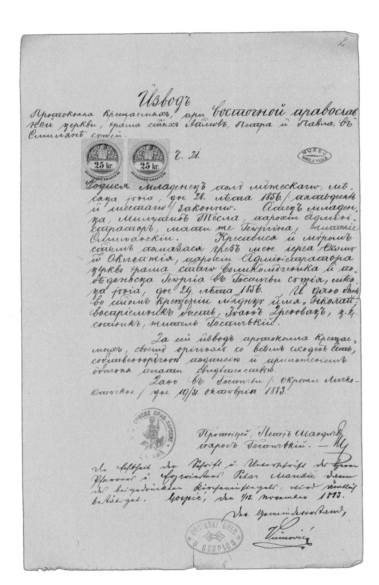

Birth Certificate issued on 31st October 1883
by the Serbian Orthodox Church in Smiljan

Auszug,

aus der Taufmatrikel der Pfarrkirche zu den h. Aposteln Petar u. Paulus in Smiljan.

Nro. 21.

Es wurde ein Kind männlichen Geschlechtes am 28. Juni = 10. Juli 1856 f. fünfzig u. sechs ehelich geboren. Der Vater des Kindes ist, Milutin Tesla, Pfarradministrator, u. die Mutter Georgina, Ehegatten von Smiljan. Es wurde getauft u. gefirmt durch den Priester Toma von Oklobdžija, Pfarradministrator der Kirche des h. Erzpriesters Georg in Gospić, den 29. Juni = 11. Juli 1856. Und bei der h. Taufe wurde dem Kind der Name "Nikolaus" gegeben; der Taufpate war Johann Drenovac k. k. Erzpriester Hauptmann von Gospić.

Daß dieser Taufmatrikel-Auszug seinem Originale vollkommen in Allem gleichlautend sei, bestätige ich mit meiner eigenhändigen Unterschrift u. Beidrückung des gewöhnlichen Kirchenamtssiegels.

Gegeben in Gospić, zum Ziku-Oktober Starosti / den 19/31. Oktober 1883.

(L. S.) Petar Mandić, Erzpriester u. Pfarrer in Gospić.

für die richtige Übersetzung
P. Mandić
Erzpriester

century after his death. The child was named Nikola, most likely after either his paternal or maternal grandfather, as both had the same name.

The rectory where Nikola was born was located next to the Orthodox Church in which Nikola's father Milutin served as a priest. Milutin was an intelligent and educated man, respected priest, and a poetic soul and prominent orator known throughout Lika. When the Bishop of Lika asked priests to make a sermon W D, Milutin's sermon was the best and won general recognition. For that reason, he was transferred from the position of a pastor in Senj to the position of an administrator, and later was appointed a rector in Smiljan. Milutin's house had a great atmosphere and radiated a gentleness that was emblematic of the home of a spiritual and highly educated person, in line with the best traditions of the Serbian people. As a young man and son of an officer of Napoleon's Army, Milutin was also supposed to become an officer. He was brought up and educated accordingly, as was his brother who graduated the Military Academy and became a mathematics teacher. Initially, Milutin followed the family tradition, but finding himself unsuited for the role of an officer, he used the first opportunity to leave the academy and enroll in the Theological School. He found his mission in priesthood and devoted himself to Orthodox faith. He studied philosophy, was fluent in German and Italian, and had a large library. The latter was the source of knowledge, experience and spiritual happiness not only for him but also for his children, especially Nikola. Milutin considered himself to be not only a man of the church but also somebody who could try to help his fellow citizens get a better education, improve their work productivity, and strengthen economic power. He

FMT

was a poet and a writer, and occasionally published poems and ethnographic articles in Serbian, thus contributing to the development of literacy amongst his people. Moreover, in magazines and newspapers one could find several articles authored by him on subjects such as the needs of farmers, economic conditions in Lika, Serbian schools, school curricula and other subjects related to culture and education. For instance, he pointed to the fact that Lika had many schools in the German language and advocated opening schools in the native tongue, something he also sought to write with wherever possible. He advocated justice and unselfishness, instilling those virtues in his son Nikola. Milutin was very much influenced by a Serbian philosopher, moralist and writer Dositej Obradović. He was also influenced by the Il-lyrian Movement, which fought against Hungarian control and those who supported Hungarians. Although it failed as a movement, Illyrism was successful on the cultural agenda, as it formed foundation for the Serbo-Croat language at the Vienna Conference of Serb and Croat Philologists in 1850.[4]

Milutin Tesla exerted significant influence on the upbringing and education of his children. In his autobiography, Nikola Tesla described his father as an excellent natural philosopher, poet, writer, and preacher. Nikola claimed that sermons of his father were retold for a long time and compared them with those of Abraham at Sancta Clara. He admired his father's excellent memory and ability to cite passages from books in several languages and attributed his own ability to do so to his father's genes. Milutin also helped him practice many things, from memorizing long sentences to guessing other people's thoughts. He was a huge influence in Nikola Tesla's childhood, stimulating him critically and hone his

Tesla's birthplace in Smiljan next to which is the Church of St Apostles Peter and Paul where Tesla's father Milutin Tesla held service

mental arithmetic. But, according to Nikola, he owned his gift for invention to his mother Djuka – Georgina, nee Mandić.

Tesla's mother was a daughter of an Orthodox priest, and her maternal grandfather was Lika Archpriest Toma Budisavljević. Djuka was one of seven children of Nikola Mandić and, after losing her mother at a young age, the burden of caring for the family fell on her shoulders. She was the only of seven children who did not go to school and was illiterate but loved to tell stories and recite poems. She was devoted to her children, bringing them up in the spirit of tradition and heroic past of the Serbian people. Tesla lovingly remembers his mother narrating *The Mountain Wreath* and Njegoš's philosophical thoughts.

His mother was an extraordinary woman, with an exceptional gift for invention, which has been a common trait of the Mandić family over several generations. She had a difficult life; Nikola talked with admiration about some of her bold undertakings, as when she helped her father in nursing patients suffering from severe epidemics. She invented a number of useful tools and was an excellent weaver, using the threads she spun from wool herself. A tireless woman, who worked from dawn until dark, and made by hand almost all of their clothing and furniture.

Nikola spent his earliest childhood in the churchyard of the Orthodox church in which his father served. Their house was situated next to the church, at the foot of the Bogdanići Hill, surrounded by nature. There was a large field next to the house and the church, and far on the horizon one could see the outline of Velebit Mountain, hiding the Adriatic Sea. As a boy, Nikola loved the flora and fauna of the place and suffered deeply when his family moved to the neighboring town

*Tesla's sisters – Angelina Trbojević, Milka Glumičić
and Marica Kosanović*

Gospić. As well as with his friends, he also played with his favourite seven year older brother Dane, and sisters Angelina, Milka and Marica. According to Nikola, Dane was very talented and a lot was expected from him. The joy of early childhood was darkened by a dear animal, an Arabian horse, which killed his brother in an accident. On an earlier occasion, the same horse saved his father's life, as he rode over a wolf-infested mountain. The frightened horse unseated Milutin who lost consciousness as he fell. The horse trotted back to the house, raised the alarm, and ran back to Milutin, who was just regaining consciousness. As he mounted the horse, he was met by the rescuers who told him that the horse had come for help whilst he was unconscious. The same horse killed Nikola's brother Dane and wrecked and aggrieved the family, scarring Nikola's soul and inflicting wounds that never healed. Many years after the unfortunate event, Nikola used to wake up filled with fear, suffered from hallucinations and experienced the appearance of images and flashes of light that interfered with his vision. It is possible that many of his eccentricities manifested in childhood and later were connected to the trauma of losing his brother.

Nikola's eldest Milka married the Lika priest Jovan Trbojević, his other sister Angelina married the priest Glumičić, and the youngest Marica married a Sušak priest, Nikola Kosanović.

In 1862, following his father's wish, six-year old Nikola enrolled into one-class primary school called *Trivijalka* in Smiljan, where classes were held in the native language. In other schools in Lika, under the regime of Austrian absolutism, classes were held in German. The sorrow he felt for the lost brother caused Nikola to deem his efforts worthless in comparison to his brother's achievements. He grew up with little self-confidence, although he was undoubtedly an intelligent child. Moreover, as a very small boy he became known for his good sense of humor and intelligence. There are many anecdotes illustrating his good humor, one of them about him meeting his two wrinkled faced aunts. They loved Nikola dearly, however, he feared their affection and kisses. Once, while he comfortably snuggled in his mother's arms, they asked him who of the two was prettier. Little Nikola examined them and pointing to one of them said: "She is not as ugly as the other."

Nikola respected his father, although he disliked his resolve to educate him for a clerical profession. They spent a lot of time together and Nikola even remembered funny comments his father made when referring to their walleyed servant Mane. Once, Mane was cutting the wood and scared Nikola's father who said: "For God's sake, Mane, don't strike at what you are looking at but what you intend to hit." Milutin had a habit of talking to himself, in such a quick and intense way that it sounded like he was talking to several people.

As the only son, Nikola had to have certain privileges, especially because he had only one younger sister, Marica. They were very close, and their tender relationship lasted throughout his life. He admired the big male cat and the fierce gander, which were the main protagonists of a beautiful story he wrote for Miss Pola when he was eight years old. It seems that the male cat was his first inspiration in the field of electricity. As a child, he noticed that occasionally, when he stroked the cat's back, its hair emitted sparks. We do not know if he connected this phenomenon with lightning, but we do know that his father explained to him that the sparks and the lightning were the same phenomenon – electricity. We do not know what Nikola made out of it, but we do know that he asked: *"Is nature a giant cat? If so, who strokes its back?"* Nikola's childhood experiences with natural and static electricity were the foundations for his knowledge about electrical science, in which he would make fundamental discoveries. Lightning remained his eternal fascination, and he could never have enough of high voltage, long sparks, and thunderous crashes, which filled him with admiration and awe.

Nikola also observed water of the Vaganac stream and pondered what to do with its live power manifested through constant movement and babbling. He was enchanted by the mechanical powers of water and invented some simple devices that were moved by it. For instance, he made a wooden millwheel without paddles, unlike those of 'real' water mills, which, to his delight, spun lively in the current. Later, when he saw the Krka Falls he got even more excited, and when he heard about the gigantic Niagara Falls, he told his uncle he would go there to harness its power.

Nikola admired birds, especially geese that rose in the air and flew in such a perfect formation that "*it would have put a squadron of the best aviators of the present day to shame*," Nikola wrote in his autobiographical article in 1917.[5] These geese would return from the feeding ground in the evening and would fly away again in the morning. Birds were Nikola's inspiration to do something about the flight of man. As a boy, he tried to fly with an umbrella from the roof of the house. He learned the hard way, as the umbrella turned inside out and became a simple stick in his hand, and Nikola fell so heavily that he had to spend several days in bed. Still, this experience did not dissuade him from various adventures, causing him to even risk his life more than once.

Observing May-bugs, which were pests for all fruits at a certain period of the year, Nikola got the idea to make a motor powered by these insects. He took a sliver as an axis, attached to it a wooden wheel and glued May bugs on a thread. When the glued insects started to fly and he headed them in the same direction, they turned the wheel with a large torque. The successful experiment was interrupted by appearance of his friend, a son of a retired officer, who delightfully ate some of the insects from Nikola's engine. Nikola was so nauseated that not only did he abandon the project, but, practically the very idea of being involved with insects ever again!

EDUCATION

Such were Nikola's experiences in Smiljan, involving earth, water and air. The idyllic life in nature was interrupted by the family's move to Gospić. Nikola finished the first grade of primary school in Smiljan, and as a six-year-old boy felt uncomfortable in the unknown town. It was a new and rough experience. He had to make new friends, get used to a new school, new environment, and deal with the absence of nature and many dear animals.

In his autobiography, Nikola told of his life struggle from that time: *"Up to the age of eight years, my character was weak and vacillating. I had neither courage nor strength to form a firm resolve. My feelings came in waves and surges and varied unceasingly between extremes. My wishes were of consuming force and like the heads of the hydra, they multiplied. I was oppressed by thoughts of pain in life and death and religious fear. I was swayed by superstitious belief and lived in constant dread of the spirit of evil, of ghosts and ogres and other unholy monsters of the dark. Then, all at once, there came a tremendous change which altered the course of my whole existence."*[5]

A novelty in Nikola's obviously unhappy life, tormented by powers of his personality, were the books, which he said *"of all things [I] liked [books] best."*

His father had a large library, so Nikola tried to satisfy his passion for reading whenever possible. His father did not allow him to read at night and spoil his sight, and he hid the candles when he found out that Nikola was reading in secret. However, nothing could stop Nikola. He made his own candles by casting tallow into thin candle molds, covered the door's keyhole and all the cracks, and continued to read often till dawn when his mother started her arduous daily work. Sleepless nights did not have a big impact on young Nikola and his passion would have probably exhausted him in the long run, had it not been combined with the newly made decision to finish everything he had started. On one occasion he came across a Serbian translation of a novel entitled

"*Abafi*", (the son of Aba), by the famous Hungarian writer Josika. The novel stirred up his internal being and he began to practice self-control. Tesla wrote: "*At first my resolutions faded like snow in April, but in a little while I conquered my weakness and felt a pleasure I never knew before - that of doing as I willed. In the course of time this vigorous mental exercise became second to nature. At the outset my wishes had to be subdued but gradually desire and will grew to be identical. After years of such discipline I gained so complete a mastery over myself that I toyed with passions which have meant destruction to some of the strongest men.*"[5]

At one point as a teenager, Nikola was seized by a mania for gambling, which greatly worried his parents. His father could not understand what was happening to his son and his mother was desperate. Father's reasoning, considering gambling to be a waste of time and useless idle, had no affect on Nikola. His mother was different, thanks to her wisdom and cunning, and she even gave him money once, when he returned home desperate after losing all of his own cash. This action had such an effect that Nikola gave up gambling forever. His passionate nature and will power waged war with smoking and even drinking black coffee. After he conquered those 'weaknesses', he boasted that victory over himself gave him more pleasure than smoking and drinking black coffee ever had.

Life in Gospić soon became interesting. Nikola played with other boys, made pea-shooters and arrows. As there was no big industry for children's toys, children had to be creative and find their own means of entertainment. Nikola soon became known for the quality of his pea-shooters and arrows. Unfortunately, the quality of those toys was not a good thing, as many windows were broken by stray projectiles. Furthermore, because Nikola's arrows could penetrate a board as thick as a thumb. there were many worries for possible injuries. The solid craft of those toys indicated the accuracy and creativity, which came to be demonstrated in his utterly perfected models, prototypes and facilities.

In the secondary school (Lower Real Gymnasium), Nikola had a problem with freehand drawing. That seemed strange, since he had a vivid imagination and described himself as a person capable of imagining any device in detail and being able to see a vivid and realistic picture of an object in his mind. At one point in his life, he claimed that he could not always differentiate real and imaginary visions. It appears as if Nikola had the ability to visualise objects in a "holographic", three-dimensional space. In school, he had talent for mathematics. He used to do mental arithmetic, which many found impossible and thus chose to believe that he had invented a special way of finding answers.

Nikola's most interesting venture was the creation of a special cylinder on an axis, half-immersed in a box. He did this so well, that it was possible to achieve low pressure in the box by extracting the air with a pump. Nikola expected that the air pressure would be exerted at a tangent on the surface of the cylinder and produce rotation. During the experiment, the cylinder would move just a little bit and would stop as soon as the pressure in the box fell. Nothing could make it rotate faster, and the experiment brought disappointment when he finally understood that the air pressure is exerted at right angles on the surface of the cylinder, without creating necessary tangential force. Still, many years later, it proved to be a useful experiment, as the idea of slow rotation of the cylinder, which at first encouraged him and then discouraged him, led him to the invention of his bladeless turbine. That was also an example of how research does not always have to produce valuable results. Nikola could not have known it at the time, but his intuition continued to stimulate him to research, regardless of temporary disappointments with his "great ideas".

Thirteen-year-old Nikola soon stumbled upon a discovery. He was playing with a group of friends making snowballs, which they rolled on the ground to make bigger ones. It would remain fun and nothing more if one of the big snowballs by pure chance had not become an avalanche, rolling down the hill with a loud thud. The huge snowball swept away everything in its path. This was a new experience for Nikola, which made him search for small impulses that trigger avalanche-like processes. Later, electrical and mechanical impulses were sources of many unusual processes he initiated. The most impressive examples were his impulse mechanical oscillator and the sparkling electrical oscillator, where a spark caused discharge of great energy into the condenser and created a powerful avalanche-like process, which generated millions of volts in the transformer's secondary coil.

Gospić had one river where Tesla used to swim, and which made him famous. A new fire brigade was established in the town and firefighters in new uniforms paraded the town. A ceremony was arranged for the demonstration of the new pump and firefighters' skills. Following the speeches and the parade, firefighters started to pump water using the new equipment, but there was no water coming from the nozzle, although the hose was in the river. Experts and equipment suppliers could not figure out the cause. Tesla left the crowd, ran into the river where the hose was submerged, and

Senior High School in Karlovac

removed grass that blocked the opening of the hose. Water
suddenly gushed forth, covering many unsuspecting invitees.
It was a true sensation, Tesla was celebrated as the hero of the
day, and people talked about the event for weeks afterwards.[5]

When he finished primary school in Gospić, in 1870,
Nikola was supposed to continue education in another town.
Before this new change came to life, he fell severely ill. His
father was already trying to make him accept a clerical profession, considering it to be much easier than further hard
studying. Although weak and of frail health, Nikola started
every new task with great enthusiasm. As they had already
lost a son, Nikola's parents were concerned for his health and
his exaggerated commitment to every new idea, as his illness
had already taken a grip on him. Nikola, unaware of the severity of his illness, was finding consolation and incentive

for further discoveries in the books from his father's library. In his autobiography he said that in those days of the illness he ran across one of Mark Twain's books which shook him up and ignited his will to live. Many years later he met Mark Twain and they became close friends. Tesla told Mark how his book helped him overcome depression caused by severe illness.

When he was fifteen, Nikola continued education at the High School (Higher Real Gymnasium) in Rakovac near Karlovac. Classes were held in German as it was a school within the Austro-Hungarian Military Frontier. It was the best school in the area, focusing on technical education – mathematics, physics, and chemistry. He lived in Karlovac, at his aunt's who was married to Colonel Branković, a retired officer of the Austro-Hungarian Army. Life in the new town was difficult for several reasons. In the area in which he lived there were many people ill with malaria and he constantly felt bad, despite taking medicines to fight the fever. Fearing for his health, his aunt fed him good quality food, but in such small quantities that Nikola used to say he was fed like a canary bird while he had an appetite of a wolf.

He found salvation and a source of true happiness while studying scientific subjects, especially physics. He had an excellent teacher of physics, Martin Sekulić, who wrote for the magazine "Rad", published by the Yugoslav Academy of Sciences and Arts in Zagreb. By the time, the science of electricity had already achieved significant results in the field of electrostatics and steady electric currents, including a range of inventions such as Alessandro Volta's discovery in 1800 that particular chemical reactions can produce electricity, Michael Faraday's electric dynamo in 1831, the telegraph by

Samuel Morse and a number of other scientists during the 1830s and 1840s, various constructions of electrical motors, and the installation of the undersea transatlantic telegraph cable between Europe and North America in 1858. A very important step in the development of electrical engineering of high voltage was demonstrated at the World Exhibition in Vienna Prater on May 1, 1873. It was the sixth international exhibition demonstrating a range of new electrical devices, including Gramme's generator with annular rotor, and Hafner-Alteneck dynamo machine with drum rotor. The real sensation, however, was the experiment by a French engineer Fontaine regarding transmission of electrical power from Gramme's dynamo machine to another similar machine located one kilometer away, which worked as a motor and powered a pump. That was the first long-distance transmission of power and demonstration of the reversibility of the Gramme dynamo. Professor Sekulić probably told his students about those achievements, and, as Nikola was helping in the physics laboratory, it certainly influenced his decision to pursue engineering studies. Tesla expressed his wish to study engineering both in letters to his parents and probably during summer holidays visits, but he encountered energetic opposition by his father. Milutin Tesla did not want him to interrupt the family tradition and wanted his son and heir to become a priest and educator. Young Tesla still craved adventure, but his playfulness was much more moderate than during his life in Gospić and Smiljan.

The school in Rakovac had seven grades of which Tesla finished three. The classes were held in German, but the Croatian language was also studied. Nikola passed exams from mathematics, physics and other subjects with high grades, but because of drawing classes and a 'D' grade he did not graduate with distinction. The 'occupation field' in transcript of his final exam, written in the German language, said "engineering."[2]

Europe was still being ravaged by a terrible cholera epidemics by the time he graduated from the High School in Rakovac. His parents tried to dissuade him from returning home to Gospić, but he did not listen to them and fell ill upon his return. He arrived exhausted by malaria and stoical life at his aunt's, and was easily overpowered by cholera. Soon, he was again on the edge of death, with no incentive to fight. Besides the illness, he profoundly suffered because his parents expected him to become a priest. He was not willing to live. He thought that his life had no future and he was sinking into spells, gradually falling into deeper and deeper depression. At one moment, when it seemed that he could not be saved anymore, his father rushed into the room and tried to bring him back to life. He promised he would send him to the best engineering school when he got well. It is not clear whether that promise was the only or main reason of the change of his state; however, Nikola started to recover, and his strength finally came back. Later, Tesla would say that, at the time, they were helpless and ignorant in the face of cholera, which they tried to treat with smoke, while continuing to drink infected water, leaving hundreds of people dead. He could not continue studies immediately as he was still weak. They sent him into the mountains to recover, but it also seems to have been a way to avoid serving in the Austro-Hungarian Army. As the Military Frontier was abolished, the status of Krajina changed and compulsory military service for all young men was introduced. Nikola avoided this obligation, and in all likelihood, was exempted from the service during his absence due to his delicate health.

In the spring of 1874, after nine months of illness, young Tesla was still weak and spent the whole year in Lika with his cousins. During this period he read a lot and became familiar with the opus of South-Slav authors. He was in particular fascinated by the lyrical and romantic poetry of Jovan Jovanović, who wrote under the pen name Zmaj.

II

ENGINEERING
STUDIES

GRAZ POLITECHNIC SCHOOL

Nikola went to study electrical engineering at the Polytechnic School in Graz in autumn of 1875. It was the nearest high-education school and one of the oldest and most respected institutions of its kind. At the time, a sizeable diaspora of Serbs and Croats was living in Graz, and his father hoped that his son would not feel too lonely and alienated there.

Graz had been known as a cultural and educational center, having one of the first four universities in Austria established in 1585. From 1594 to 1600, Kepler was the chair of astronomy and in 1869 Ludwig Boltzmann was appointed full professor of mathematical physics. In 1811, Archduke Johann of Austria established a high school in Graz, which was called "Joanneum" after himself. In 1864, Joanneum received the status of High Technical School with four faculties: civil engineering, mechanical engineering, chemical technology and forestry.[2]

With great enthusiasm, Nikola Tesla started a four-year program of "mechanical engineering."[6]

Data from the Matriculation Book of Nikolaus Tesla,
student at the Polytechnic School in Graz[2]

No.	DOB (D/M/Y)	Denomination	Nationality	Country, Place of Birth and Residence	Name and Station of Father or Guardian	Certificate of Finished High School, Data of the School
217	10 July 1856	Orthodox	Serb	Smiljan in Military Frontier, Gospić	Milutin Tesla, Orthodox Priest	Higher Realgymnasium in Rakovac

At the end of the First term 1875/1876 he passed examinations in eleven subjects with the highest grades, attending 46 classes a week on average – nearly twice as many as other students (See Table 1). Nikola expected to be praised for good work, but his father received the news of his success without enthusiasm. Only later did Nikola discover that the reason behind his father's cold manner was his professors' letters in which they advised him to take Nikola out of school lest he would kill himself through overwork. In the first year of studies, Tesla mastered the material that was usually covered in the period of two years.[6]

Vorlesung	Std	Professor	Note
Matematik I	7	Rogner	vorzuglich
Matematik II	7	Alle	vorzuglich
Experimentalphysik	5	Poschl	vorzuglich
Organische Chemie	5	Maly	vorzuglich
Anorganische Chemie	5	Maly	vorzuglich
Zoologie	5	Graber	vorzuglich
Allgemeine Botanik	3	Leitgeb	vorzuglich
Populare Machinenlehre	2	Bartl	vorzuglich
Franzosische Sprasche	3	Plisnier	vorzuglich
Cubatur der Flachen 2	2	Rogner	vorzuglich
Politische Arithmetik	2	Rogner	vorzuglich

Table 1: *Selected subjects, weekly number of classes, names of professors and marks in the academic year 1875/76*

He returned to the Polytechnic School for the second year with less excitement, and although he registered for eleven subjects, he finished only five, attending 18 classes a week. He attends classes and gains knowledge, though far less enthusiastically compared to the first year. His second year results are shown in Table 2:

Vorlesung	Std	Professor	Note
Matematik III	6	Alle	vorzuglich
Technische Mechanik	5	Stark	vorzuglich nicht
Analytische Mechanik	2	Stark	gemeldet
Tehnische Physik	3	Poschl	vorzuglich
Mineralogie	3	Rumpf	----
Elemente der Wellentheorie	2	Poeschl	----
Theorie der Kegelschnitte	2	Pelz	----
Franz. Sprasche II	2	----	----
Englische Sprache	4	----	----
Uber Congruenzen Der Zahlen	2	Rogner	gut
Uber ausgewahlte Probleme Der politischen Arithmetrik	2	Rogner	gut

Table 2: *Selected subjects, weekly number of classes, names of professors and marks in the academic year 1876/77*

During the first year, Tesla worked with Professors Rogner, Alle and Poeschl. Tesla and Professor Alle discussed various mathematical problems. Professor Poeschl, who held the chair of experimental physics, impressed him with the accuracy with which he carried out experiments, although his physique did not seem to be suitable for such precision. In his autobiography, Tesla described Professor Poeschl in the following manner:

"Professor Poeschl was a methodical and thoroughly grounded German. He had enormous feet and hands like the paws of a bear, but all of his experiments were skillfully performed with clock-like precision and without a miss."

Once, during the demonstration of the Gramme direct current dynamo, Tesla dared state his objections to some of its defects. Professor Poeschl, who was conducting experi-

*Tesla as a student,
1874-1878*

ments on the just received machine, devoted a whole lecture to Tesla's objections and impossibility of Tesla's idea to run the machine with alternating power produced by the machine's mechanical rotation. The Gramme dynamo worked as a motor when fed by direct current from a battery and created direct current when turned by mechanical rotation to generate electricity. However, looking under the hood, as a generator the Gramme machine actually produced alternating power, and a commutator served to reroute coils of the generator, converting the alternating current in the external circuit into an impulse-based direct current. When working as a motor, direct current from the external circuit was rerouted to the coils through the commutator and alternating current flowed in the coils of the motor. Tesla's idea was logical and probably not original: if alternating current is generated and the motor again needs alternating power, what is the role of the commutator? Professor Poeschl may have thought about it himself, but probably had already made up his mind as to why it was impossible to run a motor similar to a generator if it does not have a commutator and produces alternating power. Professor's explanations of the unfeasibility of the idea made Tesla abandon his hypothesis, but only temporarily. He felt that the idea was correct and there was a possibility to construct a motor without a commutator, although it had never been done. He was searching for the way to achieve progressive shifting of magnetic poles without a commutator, by applying an appropriate form of electric current. Tesla talked about the problem of reconstructing the Gramme machine to his friend Kosta Kulišić, a student of law from Graz, who mentioned it in his book about Nikola Tesla from students' days, published in Sarajevo. An interesting fact – during the second year of his studies Tesla had his first scientific announcement about capillary tubes mentioned in the literary-scientific almanac "Srbadija", printed in Novi Sad, in 1884.[7]

In 1876, Tesla applied for the engineering studies scholarship from the Foundation of Pavle Jovanovic, Matica Srpska, but was rejected twice; first because of another excellent and much poorer student, and in the second attempt because Matica Srpska ran out of funds for engineering students.[8]

At his third year in Graz, in the academic year 1877/78, Tesla registered for ten subjects. The registration form for the third year is given in Table 3.[6]

Vorlesung	
Angewandte Mathematik	bei den
Mathematik III B	Professoren
Determinanten Theorie	nicht gemeldet;
Theorie der Kegelschnitte	wegen
Analytische Mechanik	Nichteinzahlung
Allgemeine Theoretische	des
Machinenlehre	Unterrichtsgeldes
Spezielle Theoretische	fur das
Machinenlehre	1.Semester
Physikalische Geographie	1877/78
Franzosische Sprach II B	gestrichen
Englische Sprache	

Table 3: *Registration list for winter semester 1877/78*

The registration form includes remarks that Tesla did not show up to meet with professors and that his registration was cancelled because he failed to pay the fee for the winter semester 1877/78.

In the archives of the Polytechnic School (today University of Technology in Graz), a letter dated 22nd September 1876, stated that Nikola Tesla was to receive a yearly scholarship of 420 guldens, starting with the academic year 1876/77. It also stated that the condition for the scholarship was that, upon completion of the studies, Tesla serves 8 years in the military. It is assumed that his father paid for the first year of his studies, and that military authorities awarded him a scholarship for his excellent achievement in the first year of studies. It is not clear what happened in the academic year 1876/77 and why he was not able to pay for the third year of the studies, although he was receiving the scholarship until January 1878. In a letter dated 12th March 1878, the Rectory of the Polytechnic School in Graz informed military authorities in Agram (today Zagreb) that Tesla had been deleted from the registry of students. In a letter dated 4th May 1878, military authorities instructed the Rectory to stop the payment of scholarship to Tesla.[6]

After he lost his scholarship, Tesla left his studies and Graz. At one point he disappeared and no one knew where he was. A friend met him by chance in Maribor, where Tesla tried to find a job with no success; it is not known what exactly he was doing during that period. After another friend, Banjanin, informed Tesla's parents of his whereabouts, his father convinced him to return to Gospić and continue studies at Prague, the only Slav University within Austro-Hungary. Tesla reluctantly returned to Gospić and after his father's death left for Prague, in 1880.

Recently published research about the time Tesla spent in Prague found that he entered the University in Prague in the summer semester 1880.[6] He registered for three courses: mathematics, physics and philosophy, with the attendance of seven classes a week (Table 4). There is no evidence as to his attending and passing these courses, or his paying of the respective fees.

Vorlesung	Std	Professor
Analytische Geometrie des Raumes	2	Durege
Cviceni v experimentalni fysike	2	Domalip
Zahlenlotterie	2	Puchta
Uber David Hume's "Untersuchung Des menschlichen Verstandes"	1	Stumpf

Table 4: *Subjects enrolled by Nikola Tesla in the summer semester 1880*

Karolinum – Karl's University in Prague

The table shows that besides lectures in German he also attended the ones in the Czech language, however, details of his stay in Prague are still not known. One thing that is almost certain is that he did not receive a degree at the University of Prague, but this did not mean that his dedication to creating a motor with a commutator had ceased. And, as he said in his autobiography, Nikola Tesla made an important step in Prague, separating commutators from the generator and motor with the intention of finally eliminating them.[5] Finally he struck gold with the addition of extra coils to the generator and motor, something that proved to be the final piece of the puzzle.

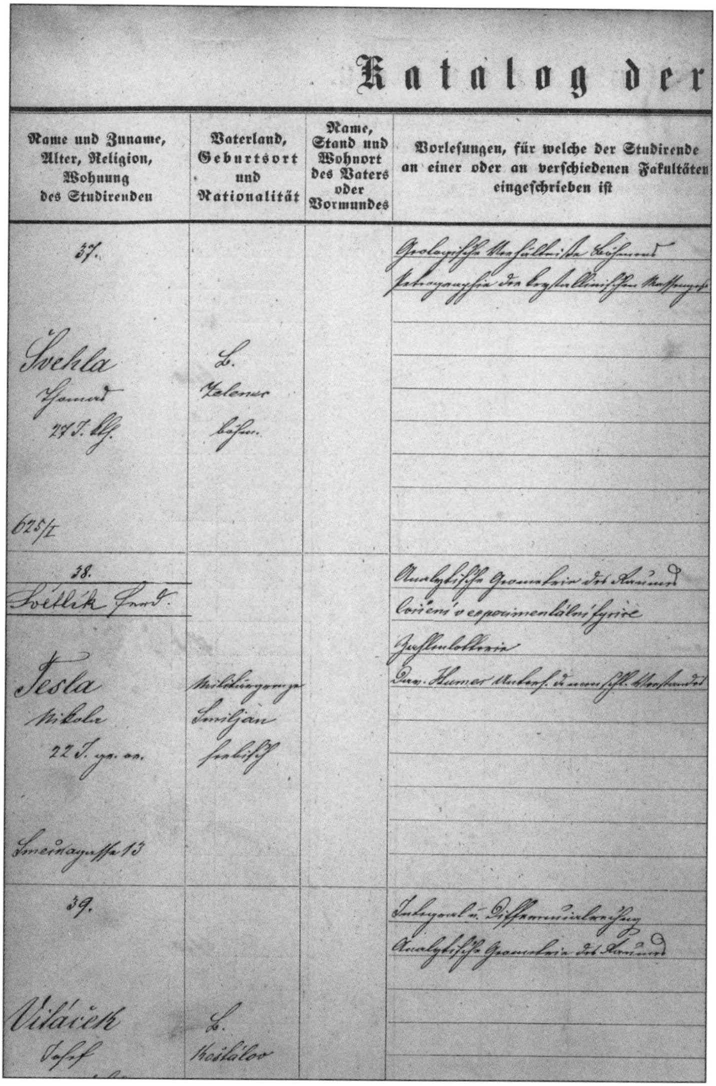

Katalog der

Name und Zuname, Alter, Religion, Wohnung des Studirenden	Vaterland, Geburtsort und Nationalität	Name, Stand und Wohnort des Vaters oder Vormundes	Vorlesungen, für welche der Studirende an einer oder an verschiedenen Fakultäten eingeschrieben ist
37. Švehla			
38. Tesla Nikola 22 J. gr. or.	Smiljan		
39. Viláček			

The Matriculation Book of Nikola Tesla issued by the University of Prague

III

FIRST
EMPLOYMENTS
IN EUROPE

FIRST EMPLOYMENT
IN BUDAPEST

After one year in Prague, Tesla's life changed. As he did not want to be a burden to his cousins, he decided to find a job. Tesla's uncle, Paja Mandić, who lived in Budapest, convinced his friend from the Officers' Academy, Ferenc Puskas, to employ Tesla in the Hungarian Central Telegraph Office. Tesla started to work as a draftsman in January 1881. This was the job he least wanted, but he had no choice. Fortunately, he was soon transferred to a more responsible position and was involved in designing plans and making cost estimates for a new telephone exchange. Although he had not regularly attended university over the past years, he obviously learnt a lot during that time and soon after joining he started making various improvements to the telephone exchange. In fact, his inventions related to voice amplification – something he never protected as intellectual property – paved the way for critical technological progress in the area. Whether because of hard work, or general situation he was experiencing, Nikola fell severely ill and suffered profoundly from an unusual sensitivity of the nervous system. In spite of taking tranquilizers, his senses of hearing, sight and touch were several times more sensitive than normal. Tesla claimed that he had always had extraordinary sight and hearing, but during this particular illness his hearing was so sensitive that a fly alighting on a table would sound as a thud. A beam of light would horrify him, while in darkness he could still perceive the presence of objects at a great distance. After a long and stressful struggle to overcome this illness, he started to recover in 1882.

INVENTION OF THE ROTATING MAGNETIC FIELD

While working at the Budapest telephone exchange, Tesla befriended Antal Szigety, who stayed with him for many years and was his loyal assistant. Once, during a walk in the City Park with Szigety, Tesla recited poetry. The sunset reminded him of the famous love verses from Goethe's Faust:

"...The glow retreats, done is the day of toil;
It yonder hastes, new fields of life exploring;
Ah, that no wing can lift me from the soil,
Upon its track to follow, follow soaring...
A glorious dream! though now the glories fade.
Alas! The wings that lift the mind no aid
Of wings to lift the body can bequeath me."

The idea of a rotating magnetic field came as a flash of lightning. He finally understood why simple alternating current could not directly power the motor. At the same time, he discovered that alternating currents generated in different phases, induced in the same generator, in different circuits, could achieve a rotating magnetic field within the motor's stator windings. The idea was simple in essence, so he was able to explain this great invention while walking with his friend. Alternating current flowing within a single coil can modify amplitude of the magnetic field it creates, but the magnetic poles remain fixed to the axis of the coil. What makes Tesla's idea so brilliant is that he used properly arranged coils to combine at least two magnetic fields created by the same frequency of alternating currents, which were out of phase with each other. Two magnetic fields add vectorially and when two sinusoidal currents of adequate phases are used, the resulting field has the same intensity, but rotates with an angular speed, which depends on the frequency of the alternating current. By using two magnetic fields with the 50Hz alternating current, the angular speed of the rotating field would be 50 revolutions per second.

By increasing the number of magnetic poles, the angular speed of the rotating field can be decreased significantly. Seven years later, Tesla's friend Szigety described these conversations from City Park and submitted technical drawings that explain ideas outlined in Budapest in 1882.[10] Tesla created a graphical diagram of the magnetic rotating field created by a two-phase alternating current in his most famous patent from 1887 (Patent Number 381,968).

EDISON CONTINENTAL COMPANY IN PARIS

It is not clear to what extent did Tesla spread information about his invention of the rotating magnetic field while in Budapest as he did not manage to find anybody seriously interested in his invention. It happened that Ferenc Puskas's brother Tivadar worked at Continental Edison Company in Paris. In the fall of 1882, helped by a reference from Puskas, Tesla was offered a job with the Continental Edison Company

Plates with the names of scientists who contributed to the development of science placed at the front and in the atrium of the "Electricite de Strasbourg" building in Strasbourg

and moved to Paris. His job role was to repair various machines produced and installed by the company.

Paris fascinated Tesla with its beauty and attractions; however, he approached his work with utmost deliberation. He would wake up early in the morning, walk from Boulevard St. Marcel to a bathing house on the Seine, swim across several times, and then walk to Ivry, where the factory was located. He worked at the factory most of the time, complemented with travels to cities in France and Germany, repairing electrical power plants and installations. Being Tesla, he presented a number of suggestions for improvements of electrical machines and was promised a good compensation.

Occasionally he would find somebody willing to listen to his ideas about his alternating power motor, but nobody that would suggest serious business deals.

Several months into his new job, in 1883 Tesla was dispatched to Strasbourg to resolve a serious defect in a power plant as it was being commissioned into production. A short circuit had damaged the power plant and ended blowing out a large part of a wall in the presence of Emperor William I during the opening ceremony. German government refused to accept the power plant and Edison's company faced a heavy loss.[5]

Due to the severity of the issue and its political implications, Tesla remained at Strasbourg for several months, giving him an opportunity to meet with a number of inventors and scientists who happened to be there at the time and subsequently became famous. Many years later, on the front of the building "Electricité de Strasbourg" Tesla's name stands together with the names of Watt, Joule, Arago, Laplace, Kirchhoff...

He never gave up his idea on the rotating magnetic field so in his leisure time at Strasbourg he and his mechanic Szigety continued to create prototypes, and finally succeeded to create the first alternating-current motor that functioned perfectly. Describing those events, Tesla said he was excited about this success, but not as nearly as the delirium of joy following the revelation of the principle that created a rotating magnetic field – the driving force of an alternating-current motor. Tesla was a very sociable person and he made many friends while in Strasbourg. His friends tried to help him with the development of the motor, however, there was no interest or understanding on the part of those who could financially support him. Thus, he was anxious to return to Paris as soon as possible, but was forced to stay in Strasbourg much longer than he had expected, due to various administrative problems. Finally, in the spring of 1884, his assignment was completed, the power plant was formally accepted, and Tesla returned to Paris with optimistic anticipations. He expected a substantial compensation promised by one of the administrators for the successful completion of the assignment in Strasbourg and for numerous improvements made to machines and regulators produced by the company. His disappointment was vast as he realised that he was deceived, and immediately decided to leave the company. A reference letter from Edison's friend Charles Bachelor was his most valuable asset as he left for America.

As he was boarding the train to take him to the the harbour, Tesla discovered that his rail and ship tickets were missing. His only possessions were several poems and technical articles, and calculations for an unsolvable integral related to his flying machine. He was eventually permitted to embark the ship only after nobody showed up to claim his reservation. It was an uncomfortable journey, as he had inadequate clothing, no money or luggage. His desire to reach the United States and meet the great master of electricity Edison was so passionate, making an awkward journey just a passing inconvenience.[5]

IV

IN AMERICA

FIRST IMPRESSIONS OF AMERICA

Tesla's autobiography vividly described his initial impression of America after arriving on 6th July 1884.[5]

"In the Arabian Tales I read how a genie transported people into a land of dreams to live thru delightful adventures. My case was just the reverse. The genie had carried me from a world of dreams into one of realities. What I had left was beautiful, artistic and fascinating in every way; what I saw here was machined, rough and unattractive. A burly policeman was twirling his stick, which looked to me as big as a log. I approached him politely with the request to direct me. 'Six blocks down, then to the left,' he said, with murder in his eyes. 'Is this America?' I asked myself in painful surprise. 'It is a century behind Europe in civilization.' When I went abroad in 1889 - five years having elapsed since my arrival here - I became convinced that it was more than one hundred years ahead of Europe and nothing has happened to this day to change my opinion."

Immediately upon arrival, Tesla went to Thomas Edison's office. He had great expectations, believing he had arrived at the right place, to meet the right man, who will immediately understand how valuable his polyphase system is and help him realise his ideas. We do not know for sure how he imagined the meeting would go, and whether he really thought that the creator and owner of the first practical system for production, transmission and use of electricity based on direct current would support him. They probably mentioned alternating current, but it was very unlikely that Edison would embrace Tesla's ideas, as his company had been dedicated to the exploration and use of direct current systems. Nevertheless, Tesla was impressed by Edison and had second thoughts whether he wasted his time learning languages and readings heaps of books, while Edison achieved so much by making utmost use of his gift for invention with limited education. Soon, however, he discovered that his formal education gave him a great advantage.

Edison realised that the man standing in front of him was a very capable person and offered him a job. Tesla's initial assignment was to repair and redesign direct-current machines, distribution systems and motors. As he had already gained experience working for Edison Continental Company in Paris and Strasbourg, he did his job successfully and easily. At that time, the famous power plant at 257 Pearl Street in New York had already been working for two years. It was the first big thermo-electric power plant: the basement contained storage for coal and space for the disposal of ashes, the ground floor contained steam boilers, and the first floor had steam machines that powered direct current generators. Generator units had around 100 horsepower, which was a comparably large system at the time. Edison made a larger system for the Paris International Electrical Exhibition in 1881, that was subsequently transferred to Edison's factory at Ivry-sur-Seine, where Tesla had worked from 1882. Soon after, Edison signed contracts for the installation of similar systems in opera houses in Paris, Berlin and Milan, actively promoting the use of his systems in Europe. He followed with England, with a deployment of an even larger, "jumbo" system of 200 horsepower, and twelve smaller units for the illumination of the 1882 Crystal Palace exhibition in London.

Tesla at the time of arrival to the United States of America

The "jumbo" system become a template for building central power stations. It was subsequently doubled in size, but remained much smaller than the power station built on Pearl Street in New York, hosting six large generators made operational at the beginning of July 1882.[12] The success in England not only promoted Edison in Europe, but was also a learning experience later used in the construction of the large central station in New York.

Soon after he arrived to New York, Tesla was given the difficult task of checking and repairing generators on the steamship "Oregon", which could no depart due to a fault in electrical systems. Tesla boarded the ship, taking with him technicians and tools he thought he would need. It turned out that the generators could not be removed, but had to be repaired on the spot, under very difficult conditions. Persistent as he was, Tesla worked through the night and managed to repair both generators and enable the ship to steam out. On his way home, he met Edison and his associates who were going to work. To Edison's remark that a young Parisian was running around at night, Tesla responded that he had just repaired the generators and that the ship had departed. Edison was amazed and, as he rejoined the group, whispered something to the effect of "damn good man."

From then on, Tesla gained great reputation and received huge praise from Edison: "I have had many hard-working assistants, but you take the cake", having in mind Tesla's persistence, endurance, and his inordinate ability to resolve problems. Not too surprising, given that Tesla worked ridiculously long hours, 10:30am to 5am the following day coupled with an innate ability to detangle the uncomprehensive. It seems that throughout this time Tesla did not manage to present in detail his alternating-current motor to Edison. It is probable that they talked shortly on the subject, but, obviously, Edison did not show any interest for rival alternating currents. Tesla also expected a promised bonus for successful reconstructions of Edison's machines, but alas; yet again he felt deceived and resigned, starting a new journey into the unknown. He had to find alternative ways to secure initial capital for the development of the system he invented. His engagement with Edison proved to be a good experience, not only in terms of learning about business and American spirit, but also gave him knowledge of direct-current machines, which was an inspiration and incentive for his future patents.

TESLA'S COMPANIES

After he left Edison, at the urging of friends, Tesla established the arc light company in 1885. In essence, he wanted to use this company to start developing his polyphase system, but his partners stressed that they were only interested in arc light production. The company was called *"Tesla Electric Light and Manufacturing Company"* and started working at the end of March 1885. Use of electricity for illumination had been steadily increasing, utilising bulbs with incandescent filament operating in low pressure gas, as well as arc lamps operating under normal air pressure. Edison was the most successful producer of bulbs with incandescent filaments, most often made of carbon.[12] With his new company, Tesla made experiments with arc lamps and designed several successful automatic arc lamps powered by direct current. Additionally, he developed special commutators with reduced sparking, and produced a new type of generator that used auxiliary brushes to regulate the power, later extensively used by car manufacturers. He submitted patents for three inventions in 1885, five in 1886, and two in 1887, before applying for a patent on his major inventions in the field of polyphase currents, on 12th October 1887. His first company went into bankruptcy in 1886, at the time of a great crisis in America. Tesla went through a very difficult period and had to do manual work in order to survive. Then he met Mr. Brown, manager of the *"Western Union Telegraph Company,"* who was interested in alternating currents. Mr. Brown managed to secure a loan of half a million dollars and established a joint company *"The Tesla Electric Company"* in April 1887. Tesla located the laboratory on Liberty Street and the office on South Fifth Avenue,

Four-pole electromagnetic motor (the asynchronous motor with a short-circuit rotor), presented by Tesla in his lecture before AIEE held on May 16, 1888.

only a few blocks away from Edison's workshop. In an amazingly short time, Tesla created an entire range of different types of motors and generators utilising his new polyphase alternating current system. Four years had passed since the day he developed his first alternating current motor in Strasbourg, and now he finally got the chance to turn it into reality. Unfortunately, these items have not been preserved in his legacy, which was transferred to Belgrade after his death and is currently located at the Nikola Tesla Museum; only a few torus coils were found, most likely used for polyphase current experiments.

Science Museum in London exhibits a model of a twelve-pole induction motor, which Tesla gave to professor Ayrton during his visit to England in 1892. Original photos of this and several other models have been preserved, remaining the only traces of Tesla's great engineering skill.[9] The twelve-pole induction motor was designed to use polyphase currents of 50V per phase, and could function with two, three, four, or six phases. The poles of the stator were protruding, and the rotor had short-circuited windings. Two models were made at the Nikola Tesla museum based on the original photos of Tesla's models: a two-phase induction motor with four torus coils and an iron plate rotor, and another similar motor, which was tested by professor William A. Anthony from Cornell University, who published data on its efficiency, speed and torque.

LECTURE ON ALTERNATING CURRENTS MOTORS AND TRANSFORMERS

Tesla started applying for patents related to polyphase systems and various types of motors in October 1887. On 1st May the following year, he received the first six patents, which included the induction motor and the polyphase power transmission system. A few weeks later, 16th May 1888, he held his first lecture before the American Institute of Electrical Engineers, under the title *"A New System of Alternating Current Motors and Transformers"*.[13] In his introduction, Tesla said:

"The subject which I have the pleasure of bringing to your notice is a novel system of electric distribution and transmission of power by means of alternate currents, affording peculiar advantages, particularly in the way of motors, which I am con-

(No Model.)

N. TESLA.

ELECTRO MAGNETIC MOTOR.

4 Sheets—Sheet 3.

No. 381,968.

Patented May 1, 1888.

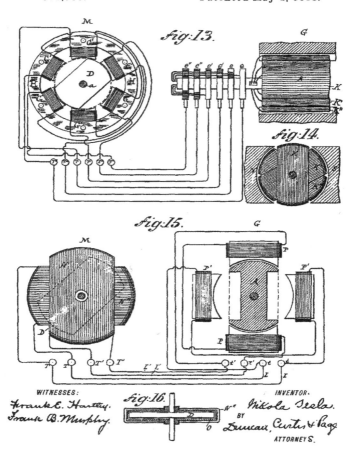

Electro-Magnetic motor – Tesla's patent no. 381.968, awarded 1st May 1888

fident will at once establish the superior adaptability of these currents to the transmission of power and will show that many results heretofore unattainable can be reached by their use; results which are very much desired in the practical operation of such systems and which cannot be accomplished by means of continuous currents."

He talked about the role of the commutator in direct current dynamo-machines and motors, and explained how to create rotating magnetic poles using alternating currents, thereby removing the need for a commutator. He used his two-phase generator and motor to explain the formation of a rotating magnetic field, similar to the Patent Number 381,968. He explained that the disc of a magnetic metal is set in rapid rotation by rotating magnetic poles. The rotation is caused by induced currents produced by the rotating magnetic field. Rotating magnetic field is a sum of magnetic fields of two currents; when current variations are sinusoidal the resulting magnetic field is of constant strength, rotated by constant angular speed. To demonstrate the application of this principle, Tesla developed two types of motors: synchronous and asynchronous. Synchronous motor had a low starting torque but maintained constant speed with any load, while the asynchronous motor had a high starting torque, but its speed depended on the load. Furthermore, Tesla invented how to start the motor in asynchronous mode and, once its speed approaches the constant synchronous speed, how to continue to operate in synchronous mode.

Tesla noticed that projecting poles increased the motor's tendency to run in synchronism and the highest torque was achieved if there were no projecting poles. For different rotation speeds Tesla mentioned the possibility of using a generator with n poles and the motor with n_1 poles. In this case, the speed of the motor will be equal to that of the generator multiplied by n/n_1.

The lecture in the American Institute of Electrical Engineering produced sensation because it shook the very foundations of Edison's efforts to have the direct-current system adopted as the universal method of using electricity for illumination and transmission of energy. By then, Edison had established a very successful business with a large number of power plants in operation across US and Europe.

Another, smaller group of scientists worked with alternating currents. One of the most remarkable amongst them was George Westinghouse, famous for the invention of the air brake. Westinghouse had some patents on single-phase alternating current generators and transformers but had not managed to make an adequate motor. He attended Tesla's lecture and became interested in the cooperation with Tesla. Their conversations were productive, as both of them were enthusiastic inventors of a similar nature. Unlike Tesla, Westinghouse was also a successful businessman, in possession of the necessary capital, as well as connections and contacts to bring inventions into life.

Two great men soon made a deal. Westinghouse bought 40 of Tesla's patents on almost all elements of polyphase system. According to Tesla's biographer, John O'Neill, Tesla received one million dollars for the transaction, and royalties per each horsepower of constructed machines. According to some calculations, royalties should have brought Tesla more than ten million dollars until the cessation of the validity of

Nikola Tesla and George Westinghouse made
a perfect partnership ➤

PERFECT PARTNERSHIP

George Westinghouse and Nikola Tesla. Seeking to make long distance electric power transmission a reality, they combined their skills, their genius and their belief in a new technology… alternating current. Together they started a revolution that electrified the world. A Perfect Partnership.

patents. Neither data from Westinghouse's Company, nor the documentation archived at the Nikola Tesla Museum in Belgrade, contains any evidence that such a contract had been signed, however, it is evident that Westinghouse did buy the patents and started with construction of motors, generators and transformers based on Tesla's design. In his book *"Prodigal Genius,"* John O'Neill states that Tesla tore to pieces the contract worth a million dollars when Westinghouse asked to be relieved from paying royalties, as his company faced merciless competition and was in danger of going into bankruptcy. Allegedly, Tesla said:

"Mr. Westinghouse, you have been my friend, you believed in me when others had no faith; you were a brave one to go ahead and pay me a million dollars when others lacked courage; you supported me when even your own engineer lacked vision to see the big things ahead that you and I saw; you have stood by me as a friend. The benefits that will come to civilization from my polyphase system mean more to me than the money involved. Mr. Westinghouse, you will save your company so that you can develop my inventions. Here is your contract and here is my contract – I will tear both of them to pieces and you will no longer have any trouble from my royalties. Is that sufficient?"

Another biographer, Margaret Cheney,[15] claims that Tesla received sixty thousand dollars (five thousand in cash and 150 shares) from Westinghouse's Company, and two and a half dollars per produced horsepower. The amount he would have received from such royalties would have been impressive; however, Tesla does not say a word about it in his autobiography written in 1919.

It is interesting to note that Tesla, probably at the urging of friends and partners, sent two models of his alternating-current motor to be tested by Professor William Anthony at Cornell University. In the discussion after Tesla's lecture before the American Institute of Electrical Engineers, Professor Anthony described his measurements of the power and efficiency coefficient of Tesla's motors: the first had a half-horsepower motor and the second had just over one horsepower. The first worked with about 50% efficiency and the stronger motor achieved efficiency above 60%.[16] Both motors had very good qualities, given that they were the first motors of this type, proving the engineering talent of their designer. Tesla undoubtedly possessed extraordinary construction skills, as he did not have to experiment with many prototypes before producing the final model. As Tesla himself said, he would visualize various designs and would "operate" them in his mind, adjusting and fine tuning until he was satisfied with the results. Only then, he would construct a physical model that would function exactly as he imagined it. Modern constructors use similar design principles, helped by numerous computer-based mathematical models and simulations before they proceed with the construction. Tesla had an extraordinary ability to perform such a simulation in his mind.

After he sold the patent rights to Westinghouse, Tesla agreed to move to Pittsburgh and take a highly paid consulting job, working with Westinghouse's engineering team to commercialise the application of his patents. Tesla soon realized that he was not cut out for that job. He was an individualist and needed freedom for unimpeded thought; he found it difficult to cooperate with other employees, as his approach was shaped by different experiences and goals. One of the key issues was the dilemma about which frequency should be used for alternating current. Tesla's opinion was that the frequency of around 60 Hz was the best compromise, taking into account the oposing requirements for the induction motor (which works best at lower frequencies) and for the transmission of electricity (where higher frequencies allow for smaller transformers). Westinghouse's engineers had more experience with transmission and believed that the motor should be adjusted to 133 Hz, the frequency of their single-phase system. Only after Tesla left Pittsburgh, they adopted Tesla's suggestion, accepting that Tesla's motor should take priority when determining the alternating current frequency.

In September 1899, Tesla returned to Europe to visit the International Exhibition held in Paris, dedicated to the 100th anniversary of the French Republic. Just before the opening of the exhibition, Eiffel Tower was completed, continuing to fascinate visitors of the city to this day. The Kingdom of Serbia had its own pavilion displaying local handicrafts, glass from the Paraćin factory and weapons from the Kragujevac Military-Technical Institute. While in Paris, Tesla met with his uncle Petar Mandić and joined him on the journey back to Gospić to visit his mother. After Gospić, he visited Gacka River falls and Plitvice Lakes falls, checking whether they could be used to produce electricity.

This is how, in his autobiography, Tesla described his impressions of the visit to Europe in 1889:

"When I went abroad in 1889 - five years having elapsed since my arrival here - I became convinced that it was more than one hundred years ahead of Europe and nothing has happened to this day to change my opinion." That was opposite to his initial impression of America in 1884, when he thought that America was a century behind Europe in civilization.

Newspapers and magazines in America and Europe had been writing about Tesla's research for quite some time when the first article in Serbian, "The Serb Edison (Nikola Tesla)" was published in the magazine *Branik*, in November 1889.[17] The magazine was issued in Novi Sad, and the author of the article became personally acquainted with Tesla and wrote about him as a well-known scientist abroad who "because of his modesty was not well known among our people, only to a small circle of his classmates and close relatives." A part of this article was later published by *Srpski Glas,* issued in Zadar.

Nikola Tesla became an American citizen on 31st July 1891; in his words, he appreciated American citizenship more than many scientific awards he had received. From then on, in the headings of his patents, instead of the former: *"Be it known, that I, NIKOLA TESLA, a subject of the Emperor of Austria, from Smiljan, Lika, border country of Austria-Hungary, residing in the city, county, and State of New York...,"* Tesla wrote: *"Be it known that I, NIKOLA TESLA, a citizen of the United States, residing in the borough of Manhattan, in the city, county, and State of New York..."*

The "War of the Currents" had been ongoing for some time. Westinghouse's Electric Company, which was promoting Tesla's complete polyphase system and developing the United States' electrification plan, saw its business flourish, but at the same time faced difficulties, because of the economic crisis affecting the country. Edison's followers tried to degrade alternating currents, emphasizing the dangers of high voltage and advantages of direct currents. They used unscrupulous propaganda, best illustrated by the influence on the government to use alternating current for the electric chair capital punishment. Westinghouse's position worsened when *Thomson-Houston Company* and *Edison General Electric Company* merged to form a single *General Electric Company*, creating direct competition to Westinghouse's Electric Company. He was finally forced to forego Tesla's royalties and merge with *General Electric Company*, forming a single enterprise under the name *Westinghouse's Electrical and Manufacturing Company*.[14]

LECTURE ON HIGH FREQUENCY ALTERNATING CURRENTS

Scientific research on the most efficient frequency of alternating current for industrial use was limited to the range between a few dozen to a few hundred Hertz. During practical experiments exploring the influence of frequency on the devices he constructed, Tesla could generate variable frequency currents by changing the rotation speed of the generator. Soon after his focus turned towards generation of higher frequency currents that required generators with a much higher number of poles, combined with an equally higher rotor speed. Tesla's patents include two original constructions of these machines for the production of alternating currents above 15 kHz. One such machine had about 400 poles on the stator and was designed to operate inaudible arc lamps (Patent No. 447,920). The rotor turned with the speed of 1500 revolutions per minute. The second machine was made with a specially tailored flat disc rotor and toothed type stator (Patent No. 447,921). Experiments on those machines revealed new and unknown properties of alternating currents, which were perfectly described by Tesla in his lecture before the American Institute

Tesla's high frequency alternator

of Electrical Engineers at Columbia College in New York, on 20th May 1891.[19] Tesla prepared several exciting experiments with the assistance of Gano Dunn. The lecture was spectacular as his experiments revealed a new world of high frequency currents and high voltages. Tesla started the lecture by saying that nature is the most captivating and most worthy subject of study and added: *"Nature has stored up in the universe infinite energy. The eternal recipient and transmitter of this energy is the ether...Of all forms of nature's energy, which ever and ever changing and moving, like a soul animates the inert universe, electricity and magnetism are perhaps the most fascinating... What is electricity, and what is magnetism?"*

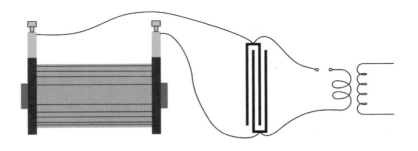

Tesla's Coil as shown at the AIEE lecture in 1891

In his lecture, Tesla considered the nature of electricity, trying to fathom the essence of the phenomenon. He presented the assumption that electricity is connected to molecular activities and stated his doubts about the existence of two types of electricity. He thought about ether as a medium that reacts differently to low and high frequency currents. He conducted experiments by gradually increasing the voltage at the ends of the transformer's secondary coil, pointing out many phenomena he tried to explain by applying his knowledge of contemporary science of electricity. He described the effects of heating a dielectric when exposed to strong fields of high frequency currents, effects of luminescence, and light effects in the vacuum and gases under pressure. He explained that the emission of light was: *"due to the air molecules coming bodily in contact with the point; they are attracted and repelled, charged and discharged, and, their atomic charges being thus disturbed, vibrate and emit light waves."* It is amazing

Tesla's experiment with wireless energy transmission ▶

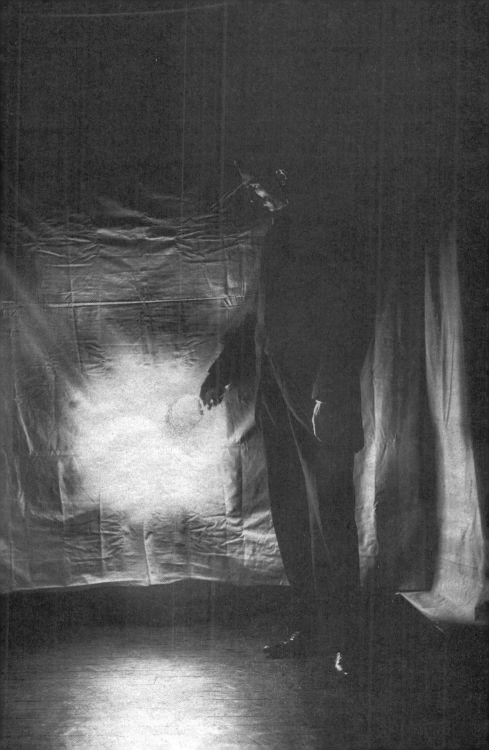

how close he was to the modern theory of the emission of light photons from atoms stimulated by an external source that is directly or indirectly caused by electricity. Tesla concluded that it would be possible to use high frequency currents to produce light and heat, as with an ordinary flame, but without consumption of material.

One of the most interesting experiments was "wireless" ignition of air-filled tubes, located in the electric field of the secondary of the resonant transformer without an iron core. That was the "Tesla Transformer," on which he applied for a patent on 25th April, a month before he delivered the lecture at Columbia College.[20] We mention this because it illustrates Tesla's way of work. He would research a subject, submit a patent application and only then would he write a paper about it or present results of the research in a lecture.

Tesla liked to surprise visitors and lab assistants with unusual and exciting experiments, such as his first demonstration of "wireless transmission of energy", powering several light emitting devices wirelessly. Helped by his assistants, he prepared a high-frequency generator, a special transformer and adequate condensers for the primary circuit, and metal plates placed on the floor and the ceiling of the laboratory that served as the condenser of the secondary circuit. Then he held two low pressure gas-filled tubes and told his associates to turn off the light and turn on the generator of high frequency currents. Everyone was shocked and fascinated by the scene that followed – tesla waving illuminated tubes as if they were swords. Later, many others repeated the experiment, leaving the observers confused and breathless. For Tesla, this

Wireless transmission of energy applied in lighting. A glass tube glows without direct contact to a source of electrical power ►

was the beginning of a new technique of cost-efficient electrical illumination, which never became applicable in practice, for many reasons that were not thought of at the time.

During the war of the currents, Tesla used high frequency and high voltage currents to counterclaim Edison's assertions that high voltage alternating currents pose danger to life. By passing high frequency currents through his body, Tesla tried to prove that Edison's claims were wrong; however, more knowledgeable audience knew that the alternating currents of lower, commonly used frequencies (e.g. 50Hz – 60Hz), as well as direct currents. could be lethal if used inappropriately. Edison's claim that many would be killed by high voltage alternating currents was merely spin, as he was trying to protect the huge investment his company made in deploying direct current systems. As we know, the standard voltages used widely today (110V – 220V) are equally dangerous, regardless of whether they are from direct or alternating current.

TESLA'S HIGH FREQUENCY CURRENT GENERATOR

We had already mentioned that Tesla applied for a patent on a new type of high frequency current generator (Patent No. 454,622).[22] Given the importance of this device and the far-reaching effect of its application, its invention deserves more attention.

Inductance and capacitance have very important roles in an alternating current circuit, and their presence is even more influential in the currents of high frequencies. Tesla was in particular enthusiastic about the role of capacitance and inductance in resonant circuits and he saw many possibilities in them. Using the known effect of oscillatory discharge of a charged Leyden jar (condenser) across the induction coil through electric spark, Tesla replaced the coil with a transformer without an iron core, with loosely coupled inductive secondary and so created a new type of generator, known as the *"Tesla Coil"* or *"Tesla Oscillating Transformer"* or *"Tesla Transformer"*. The mentioned names have been adopted although they are not very accurate, as the name *"Tesla Transformer"* is used for a high frequency transformer with loose coupling between the primary and secondary and without an iron core which usual transformers for low frequency currents have. A complete Tesla oscillator has a special circuit with various types of spark exciters, depending on whether the oscillator is powered by a direct current circuit or an alternating current circuit of industrial frequencies. It is important to mention that from the very start of this development, the secondary coil was designed to have a high number of windings without added capacitance, except for the capacitance contained in the free terminal sometimes ending with a metal ball. The secondary coil had its 'own' capacitance and resonated at several frequencies. Tesla knew about this phenomenon and thought that the lowest of these resonances could be calculated by assuming that the total wire length in the secondary coil was approximately equal to a quarter of the wavelength.

Tesla's oscillator can be relatively easily explained at a high level, although its detailed description is extremely complex. In the following analysis we will assume that the primary and secondary circuits have been adjusted to the same resonant frequency which is determined by the Thompson formulae $\omega_0 = 1/\sqrt{L_p C_p} = 1/\sqrt{L_s C_s}$, which Tesla tried to achieve in his devices. We can assume that a source is charging the condenser of primary circuit C_p to a certain voltage V, while storing energy $C_p V^2 / 2$ in it. A maximum voltage at the terminals of the condenser determines the striking voltage of a spark gap (made of two conducting electrodes separated by a gap). At the moment of attaining the striking voltage for the selected spark gap, the gap breaks and condenser discharges energy through the primary coil of the Tesla transformer. The discharge is oscillatory, and the type of generated electricity depends on inductance and capacitance of the primary and the secondary coils and mutual coupling between the primary and the secondary circuit. A long spark, as seen on picture) causes the transfer of energy from the primary into secondary and vice versa. In that case, the attained oscillations are two dampened sinusoids, one above and the other below the selected frequency ω_0. As the coupling is tighter, the difference in frequencies is larger. If there is no new excitation – new discharge of energy from the external circuit of the condenser, oscillations stop when the initial energy is consumed and the spark quenches.

It is much more favorable when the spark in the primary circuit goes off upon the transition of energy to the secondary, as there would be no further losses in the primary and the secondary would continue to oscillate at the frequency of the secondary circuit ω_0. Tight coupling between the primary and the secondary shortens the time of energy transfer from the primary to the secondary, and results that the oscillations of the secondary are closer to the continual sinusoidal current, except during the period while the energy is transferred between the primary and the secondary, during which two dampened sinusoidal currents are created, one below and the other above frequency ω_0. From the moment when the primary circuit is broken by the cessation of spark, the oscillations in the primary stop and the primary's condenser charges with the energy from the power circuit. Once the voltage in the condenser achieves striking voltage V, the oscillation process is repeated. In practice, for a defined secondary circuit, Tesla would change the capacitance and/or inductance of the primary circuit until the sparks in the secondary circuit attained maximum intensity. He had an excellent feeling for tuning his devices, in spite of not having a theoretical explanation of such complex phenomena. When he invented the Tesla transformer in 1891, there was no theoretical analysis available for this device. A simple mathematical analysis appeared only in 1895.[21]

Performance of the Tesla oscillatory transformer depended on many elements: choice of primary and secondary resonance frequencies, the coupling coefficient, spark duration, the number of sparks per second, and the load on the secondary circuit. This device is still of great interest to many constructors. During Tesla's time, it had become common in all physics laboratories, as it is today. Besides its major attraction, generation of huge sparks in the secondary, Tesla transformer has found many practical applications in everyday life. Examples include generation of high voltage for the petrol engine ignition in cars and for various oscilloscopes. Besides these applications, Tesla transformer is used in the circuits of radio transmitters and receivers, and many other electronic devices of the modern day. The most advanced power circuits for computers are also based on the application of the Tesla transformer, which no longer features the spark gap switch, as its role was made obsolete by the invention of electron tubes and transistors.

V

VISIT TO EUROPE

LECTURES IN ENGLAND
AND FRANCE

A letter that Tesla's sister Marica sent to him from Plaš-ki in May 1891, hinted at Tesla's visit to Europe. The reason behind the visit was Tesla's interest in demonstrating his research in England, and as the news spread, he also received an invitation from France. In his autobiography, Tesla wrote that in the late 1890s he received urgent invitations, numerous honors and flattering offers from all over the world, which he refused. The demand increased even more after Tesla delivered his famous lecture *"Experiments with alternate currents of very high frequency and their application to methods of artificial illumination"* to the American Institute of Electrical Engineers at Columbia University in New York, on 20th May 1891.[19] In October 1891, at the suggestion of eight members of the Association of Electrical Engineering of the United Kingdom, Nikola Tesla was elected a foreign member of the Association. The President of the Association was William Crookes, whom Tesla held in high esteem. Finally, in 1892, Tesla decided to accept the invitation of the Association of Electrical Engineers from London, and the French Society of Physicists from Paris. He prepared new experiments and adequate devices, as well as the lecture on *"Experiments with alternate currents of high potential and high frequency."* The lecture was unusually long, lasting between two and three hours, but nobody complained as the experiments were breathtaking. Tesla was renowned for his excellent oratory

Lecture room in London following Tesla's lecture in 1892

skills, and his audience was captivated by the precision and the thought process present in every aspect of the lecture. He started the lecture by holding tubes with rarefied gas, which became illuminated when he used his body as a connection with a terminal conveying alternating currents of high frequency. Through the currents that flowed though his body, he illuminated pear-shaped tubes with a small sphere, which was brought to incandescence and became an efficient light source. He described in detail his spark gap generator and its improvements achieved through fast break of the spark by the magnetic field or compressed air or by the means of divided spark gap technique. These were later "invented" by other researchers, and many books and articles fail to mention that the technique of the fast spark gap switch was actually invented by Tesla. We mention this because of the fact that the spark generator was for a long time dominant in the field of radio-technology, practically for about twenty years, until the improvement of high-power electron tubes. This invention undoubtedly proved that Tesla established some fundamental solutions, but as he did not commercialized them himself, others declared them as their own inventions, often not even mentioning Tesla. Something similar happened with Tesla's high frequency alternators, which were technically improved and introduced into practice by Alexanderson, although in this case Tesla's fundamental discovery was not neglected.

In the London lecture, special attention was given to the vacuum tube with sensitive beam-like emanation, which Tesla described as a brush discharge. He was excited about this invention and subjected it to a detailed analysis. His explanation of the phenomenon was not easily conveyed, however, as it mostly related to the description of what happens when a glass globe with central electrode is connected to the terminal of the high frequency alternator. The phenomenon had the elements of instability and it seemed the results could not be reproduced with certainty. Therefore, Tesla marked this discovery as a beginning of an important invention that could help towards development of a sensitive device for detection of weak signals, such as the signals used in telegraphy. Despite the detailed description, the audience was left without a reliable answer as to how such a device would operate. One should not forget that the then knowledge of the nature of electrical phenomena in a vacuum was very limited, and it was certainly not Tesla's specialty. Only after the discovery of electrons, several years later, did Tesla's tube with brush discharge become comprehendible and recognized as the forerunner of electron tubes. It is assumed that Tesla's brush discharge was mainly a beam of electrons and that is why it was sensitive to the influence of electric or magnetic field. In that sense, Tesla's tube with brush discharge is similar to the electron tube diode, and when reacting to electric or magnetic fields, it is similar to triode or cathode-ray tube. It is interesting that Tesla's vacuum tube could not be activated by connection to the terminal of the spark gap oscillator, as it required continuous alternating current. Tesla thought it was possible to use unipolar impulses or even continuous direct current. Judging from his words, one could conclude that Tesla thought that his vacuum tube could work as a rectifier of alternating currents.

During the lecture, Tesla demonstrated the operation of his vacuum tubes of various constructions, with small spheres positioned at the center of larger globes, made of various materials such as carbon, silicon carbide, ruby, diamante, platinum, etc. He held an unusual conviction that melted ruby sphere would emit three types of rays: the ordinary one which is visible, and two types of invisible rays, one being the ordinary wavelengths, and the other having waves of a well-defined character. He associated the relative rations of those discharges with the manner of their excitement, that is, the frequency of currents that produce the discharges. Tesla argued that higher frequencies require shorter and thicker filaments than lower frequencies. He accurately asserted that it is the consequence of unequal distribution of electricity that is dependant on frequency, today easily interpreted through "skin effect." Tesla noticed this effect in all high frequency current circuits and was probably the first to explain it, based

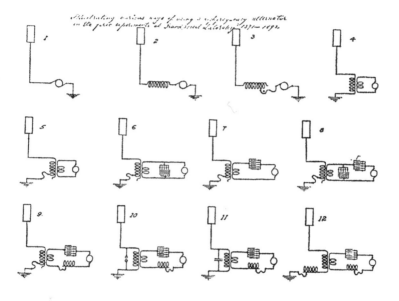

Illustration from the Nikola Tesla Museum presenting the development of connectivity options between a generator and an antenna-ground system, starting with simple connectivity (1), advancing to (12) utilising two tuned circuits coupled through a Tesla transformer.

on his intuition that a conductor may serve as an insulator if the frequency of the currents flowing through the conductor is extremely high. In developing this idea, Tesla formed the hypothesis that the material that serves as a conductor at low frequencies may become an insulator at very high frequencies, and would obtain the properties of phosphorescence. Immediately afterwards, he gave another explanation, claiming it is possible that an unheated sphere emits a visible discharge in some places (points of impact by atoms, molecules).

After various assumptions and experiment analyses, he made the important conclusion for the construction of single terminal tubes with a sphere, with efficiency twenty times higher than that of ordinary tubes with incandescent filament. *"The production of a small electrode capable of withstanding enormous temperatures I regard as of the greatest importance in the manufacture of light,"* claimed Tesla in his lecture. He added that the excitement requires high frequency currents, and that, besides the sphere that is heated at a high temperature, one has to bring the mass of the gas surrounding the electrode to the highest possible incandescence. We do not know how many such tubes Tesla demonstrated during his talk, except that the published text of the lecture contained drawings of about twenty different types. At the end of the lecture he showed two constructions of dual terminal lamps being driven through a wire connected to a Tesla coil. It is not known whether single terminal lamps had ever been produced, however, dual terminal lamps have become reality. They are really cost-efficient, as they consume at least five to six times less energy for the same quantity of light than bulbs with the incandescent filament.

Besides the tubes for light production and tubes with brush discharge, Tesla demonstrated his motor for high frequency currents, charged through one wire only. He also applied the parallel connection between induction and insulated metal plate – "antenna" in order to show how high current can flow through a single wire connected to the terminal of the high frequency generator and melt the wire, although there is no closed circuit. It was a series oscillatory circuit, consisting of inductance and capacitance, which when in resonance with the frequency of the generator, enters series resonance and has maximum current. Working on the issues of impedance in alternating current circuits, Tesla dealt with the impedance of rarified gas tubes. Through experiments he established that despite metal wire pulled through a tube, the conductor does not make a short circuit and rarefied gas lights as if there was no conductor. Tesla concluded that rarefied gas could be a better conductor of the high frequency current than a metal conductor. Taking this thinking forward, he came to a conclusion that high frequency currents could be transmitted through gas pipes, which could support surface waves. On another occasion he said that the best way of protection from lightning rod discharge would be by the means of an adequately prepared gas drain system that would become conductor for the thunder. Such system could be a unique protector of electric discharge, but it is unknown whether anybody ever tried to construct it.

At this point, Tesla only briefly mentioned the issue of wireless transmission, as a future accomplishment. During discussion on high frequency power, he talked about a conductor that would convey power at a distance. Tesla explained that it would require a thin conductor that is heavily insulated and wrapped with metal screen broken up into insulated short lengths, which should be significantly shorter than the wavelength. Such a structure without screen is known today as the Goubau surface wave transmission line, which was later tested both theoretically and experimentally. However, Tesla's name has never been mentioned in relation to it.

The lecture we outlined here resulted in great interest by the English scientists. The engineering journals however were rather reserved in extending recognition to Tesla for his invention of rotating magnetic field, polyphase currents and various alternating power motors. Tesla was received by many famous scientists during his London visit; he delivered the lecture and had plans to leave for Paris straight after. However, immediately after the lecture, Sir James Dewar invited Tesla to visit the Royal Institute, and devised a cunning plan to convince him to repeat the lecture before this Institute. As a host, he escorted Tesla to Faraday's chair, seated him in it and then poured him a glass of whiskey, Faraday's favored drink. After he told Tesla that nobody in the world deserved such an honor before, Tesla gave in and repeated his lecture before even more renowned group of scientists on 4th February 1892. The President of the Royal Institute, Lord Rayleigh, was deeply impressed by Tesla's lecture and experiments, and suggested that Tesla should concentrate on one great idea, as he was a natural born inventor. It is probable that Tesla listened to this advice, as his later research was focused on the solution of the problem of wireless energy transmission, which he considered to be the ultimate endeavor of immense value for the benefit of humankind.

This is how Tesla's lecture before the Royal Institution was reported by English journal "Engineering" on the next day: *"On Wednesday evening, the Royal Institution held one of its famous meetings for which it acquired fame... Mr. Tesla started his lecture with the words of recognition for the work of Professor Crookes who had inspired him when he was a student and who had set his work on course. Then he moved on to his own research work and in one second showed his audience how far ahead he was in relation to his predecessors..."*

Meeting with English scientists encouraged Tesla to continue experiments in the field of high frequency currents upon his return to the States. He was especially influenced by Lord Rayleigh, who suggested that he concentrate on one great idea. It seems that wireless transmission of electric power turned out to be Tesla's great idea to which he dedicated years of work.

On 19th February 1892, Tesla repeated the London lecture before the French Society of Physicists and International Society of Electrical Engineers. This lecture was attended by André-Eugène Blondel, a French physicist who years later delivered a lecture in Belgrade, in 1936, on the occasion of Nikola Tesla's 80th birthday. Referring to Tesla's lecture held in Paris in 1892, Blondel described his performance before the fascinated audience of leading scientific and engineering figures: "Tall, thin, elegant, inspired, speaking perfect French with no accent and with ease, Tesla looked like a real wizard who was revealing to his bewildered audience a new world of phenomena which they could not have imagined." Tesla's possible follow up contacts with French scientists are unknown, but he did receive numerous recognitions in the period between 1936 and 1938, including an honorary doctorate of the University of Paris (1937), University of Poitiers (1937) and University of Grenoble (1938).[22]

When Tesla returned to the hotel after the Paris lecture, he received a word that his mother was very ill. Very worried, he immediately left for Gospić.

VISIT TO HOMELAND

According to Tesla's autobiography, he arrived in Gospić in mid-April 1892. It is not clear where he was in the period between leaving Paris, around 20 February, and his arrival to Gospić.[23] He found his mother alive, but it seems she died on the second day after his arrival, on 16th April 1892. Immediately afterwards, Tesla fell ill and left for a two-week visit to his sister Marica in Plaški, and from there to Monastery Gomirje, to visit his uncle Petar Mandić, the Prior of the Monastery. He also visited his relatives in Raduč. While in Gospić, he sent a letter to his uncle Paja Mandić, expressing his sorrow: *"I am immeasurably sad, but console myself the best I can. I had long anticipated this sad event, but the blow, nevertheless, was heavy. I always hoped that mother would live longer, because she was strong, and mine and my uncle's successes were strength to her."*[23]

After the rest, joined by his uncle Petar Mandić, Tesla leaves for Zagreb on invitation of the Mayor of Zagreb, Dr. Armuš. On 22nd May 1892, he held a lecture at the Zagreb City Hall about his new polyphase system of alternating currents and recommended its use. He also met with Serbian students and received telegrams from professors of the Great School and Association of Electrical Engineers of Belgrade.

Tesla left Zagreb for Varaždin on 25th May 1892, where he spent two days visiting his other uncle, Paja Mandić, a high-ranking officer of the Austrian Army. From Varaždin, Tesla went to Budapest in order to present his view on the introduction of electrical illumination. While in Budapest, he met with the delegation of the Belgrade municipality and Association of Engineers who invited him to visit Belgrade. He accepted their invitation and arrived in Belgrade on 1st June 1892.

Tesla's arrival in Belgrade was reported by *"Srbobran"*[24]: "Everybody is going to the station tonight to welcome the great scientist and fellow countryman Nikola Tesla. Nikola Tesla will arrive by express train from Budapest at 10 pm. The dear guest will be welcomed by the Academic Choir 'Obilić', with the flag, by military orchestra, citizens, Mayor with councilors, administration of the construction association and many other associations..." When the representatives of the Serbian government, municipality and associations in Budapest invited Tesla to visit the Serbian Capital, he said: *"All the glory which I have received lately in London and Paris, mean nothing to me compared to your welcome. The cradle of my forefathers, the Kingdom of Serbia and the City of Belgrade invite me – that is a great reward for me, and nothing in the world, nothing in my life, will be dearer to me than this recognition. I am happy that I am a Serb, and shall pride myself with this forever."*

Tesla was welcomed at the railway station with ovations, and the day after, accompanied by the Mayor and Mr. Klerić, he visited the Education Minister, Mr. Andra Nikolić. The minister introduced him to King Alexander who wanted to award him the Order of Saint Sava of the First Degree, but Tesla could not receive it as it would had meant the loss of US citizenship. After the lunch at the prominent Hotel *Imperial*, Tesla visited the Great School and, responding to welcoming remarks of the Dean, Mr. Alković, addressed the students:

"Brothers and friends. Thank you for so much attention and recognition. In you, I see the Serbian youth who will work for common good of all Serbs. You are the future of Serbia. I have, as you see and hear, remained a Serb even overseas, where I pursue my research. You need to do the same, to use your knowledge and work to raise the glory of the Serbian people in the world."[25]

Around 5.30 pm, escorted by all professors of the Great School and members of the Welcoming Committee, Nikola

Tesla walked to the Kalemegdan fortress and attended a concert organized in his honor, where the Military Orchestra of the Danube Regiment played old Serbian marches. The Academic Choir Society "Obilić" performed under conductor Josif Marinković.

At 9 pm, in a restaurant in Smutekovac, next to the Weifert Brewery, Belgrade municipal authorities organized a big reception. The reception was attended by more than a hundred invitees, including ministers, professors from all educational institutions, representatives of various corporations and associations, city councilors, the Mayor and prominent citizens.

In a friendly atmosphere, surrounded by true admirers, and clearly in a good mood, Tesla said that this wonderful reception would give him strength to continue his work and thus contribute to science and to the Serbian people. After the toasts were proposed by the Mayor, the Dean of the Great School and many others, Tesla said: *"Gentlemen! I would not be a true Serb if I did not qualify this evening among the happiest and most precious hours of my life. Ever since I left my homeland to go into the world, I have experienced successes and failures, inglorious and glorious times, happy and unhappy moments. Still, I can say that luck was on my side and that happy days prevailed over the sad ones, because I achieved great success and awards in a relatively short time… My life has been a constant struggle between agony of failure and blessing of success… There is something in me, something that could easily be a delusion, as often happens with young enthusiasts, but if I am fortunate to achieve only a few of my ideals, it will be to the benefit of the whole humankind. If all my hopes are fulfilled, the thought that it is the achievement of a Serb will be the sweetest to me. Long live the Serbdom!"*[22]

Đorđe Stanojević, Physicist, Professor at the Military Academy and High School in Belgrade, later became Dean of Philosophical Faculty and Chancellor of the University of Belgrade. He was the author of the first book on Tesla written in Serbian language, "Nikola Tesla and His Inventions", published in 1984 in Belgrade

After Tesla, the floor was given to Djordje Stanojević, Professor at the Military Academy, who briefly explained the essence of Tesla's work in the field of electrical engineering and his contribution to science, in language familiar to the wide public. It was really a lecture about direct and alternating currents and an ode to Tesla's efforts to research the field of electrical engineering in order to transform everyday human life. The professor finished by saying that "such transformation will not be and cannot be produced by anybody else but our brother Nikola Tesla."

After the address of the Engineering Association, a poetic toast was proposed by respected and favorite poet Jovan Jovanović Zmaj, who was deeply touched, and for the first time in his life recited his own verses, a greeting poem dedicated to Tesla's visit, beginning with the words:

> I don't know if it's real,
> Or just a thought,
> As soon as we heard you coming,
> You electrified us

Deeply moved by the poem, Tesla kissed Zmaj's hand. In an outburst of excitement, Tesla recounted some of the stories from the beginning of his work, when his first, long prepared experiment failed and how he later found the solution. He compared those *"happy moments of joy and success"* with the moments following the recital of Zmaj's poem.

Tesla stayed until late that night, and left Belgrade early next morning, accompanied by Djordje Stanojević. He promised, and indeed intended to visit again, but that wish never came true.

During his stay in Belgrade, Tesla made an agreement with Professor Djordje Stanojević about publishing a book in Serbian, which would include a review of his work. Upon his return to the States, Tesla sent matrices with photos and original lectures. The first book in Serbian, "Nikola Tesla and His Inventions", was published in Belgrade in 1894, and was translated and edited by Djordje Stanojević, who also wrote a comprehensive introduction. Since the publication was somewhat delayed, the book also included Tesla's subsequent lecture held in the States in 1893. In the States, a book including the same lectures was edited by Thomas Commerford Martin, the President of the American Association of Electrical Engineers. This book was published in New York 1894, under the title "Inventions, Researches and Writings of Nikola Tesla,"[26] and was dedicated to Tesla's fellow countrymen in Eastern Europe.

Upon his return to the States, Tesla wrote an article for the 'Century' magazine, "Zmaj Jovan Jovanović – the Greatest Serbian Poet of Today". Tesla later translated some of Zmaj's poems, which were recast by his friend Robert Underwood Johnson and then published in the collections of poems by R.U. Johnson in 1897 and 1923, with a foreword by Nikola Tesla.

The visit to Europe enhanced Tesla's glory. He was given a warm welcome when he arrived in New York at the end of August. He refused all invitations and honors and went to the Hotel Gerlach to think in solitude, while surrounded by a buzzing multimillion beehive that was New York. Tesla gathered new energy and continued the research that had already made him famous.

VI
GREAT INVENTIONS

BASIC RADIO PRINCIPLE

Although Tesla's investigations were aimed primarily at solving practical problems, the scope of his research expanded over time. When he talked about alternating currents, he never missed the chance to mention that oscillations, resonances, and other phenomena were inherent part of the universe. He searched for universal connections between natural phenomena by observing analogies. He successfully explained behaviours of electrical signals and waves by relating them to mechanical behaviours, which are, in general, easier to comprehend. He used analogies both for understanding and explaining invisible flows of currents and magnetic forces, as well as for drawing conclusions about electrical phenomena, without trying to give an explanation by applying complex mathematical models. He used his intuition and deep insight to resolve problems and has never attempted to complicate things in order to give them a more "scientific" form. He was a true master in the laboratory, resourceful experimenter and a creator of new measurement instruments and methods. Tesla had an admirable ability to select the right components and make complex adjustments of his completely new alternating current motors and high frequency transformers. Even today, these devices present design challenges to engineers who have incomparably wider theoretical knowledge, modern measurement techniques, and powerful computers at their disposal. Modern methods of mathematical and computer modelling provide simulation of a device operation and search for the best operating conditions. Our knowledge about Tesla's research leads us to conclude that he did all the calculations in his head, without a mathematical model or computer.

In February 1893, Tesla repeated his lecture *"On Light and other High Frequency Phenomena"* at the Franklin Institute in Philadelphia,[28] and a month later at the National Electric Light Association in St. Louis, held in the town concert hall accommodating 5000 seats, as the lecture auditorium was far too small for all interested attendees!

Through time, the format of his lectures had become established, exciting the audience with new and surprising experiments. Tesla would start by admiring the eye, the most sensitive of human organs, saying that *"the very soul shows itself in the eye"*. This long, general introduction was tailored to the audience, which consisted not only of scientists and electricity experts, but also of the general public who would come to see the unique Tesla and his magic experiments.

Tesla divided the technical part of the lecture into several sections, starting by describing typical devices operated by high frequency currents obtained from direct or alternating currents of low frequency, which he had developed over the course of several years. He would then continue describing the phenomena produced by electrostatic force, backed by experiments demonstrating the effects of dynamic electric field. He would pass high frequency currents through his body, show the difference between the propagation of high frequency and low frequency currents between two metal rings, and conduct experiments with a pendulum and partially covered dielectric, a metal sphere which vigorously moves and oscillates in irregular curves.

The third section would be dedicated to the description of dynamic phenomena, that is, the effects of currents in different alternating current circuits. He would demonstrate that it was possible to conduct current through a conductor by connecting it to a single terminal of high frequency source, while its other end was connected to an insulated metal plate that acted as a rudimentary form of grounded antenna. Tesla used attractive experiments to show that it was possible to transmit current through a single wire, by varying the 'load' between the source terminal and the metal insulated plate. Contemporary electricity experts understand the phenomena with which Tesla shocked his audience, but the spirit with which he conducted them continues to amaze us. Furthermore, it is not easy to understand how he came to specific conclusions, seemingly contradictory, as we know that the theory of alternating current circuits did not exist at the time. His experiments and measurement devices helped him to produce results, but the fact that he made those in a relatively short period of time gives us the impression that most of his work was based on experimentation and intuition, rather than theory. Only a scientist with a gift of a genius could have developed motors and other components of low frequency alternating current circuits using iron and copper, and then decided to discard iron and use only copper for new components designed for high frequency currents. Tesla made attempts to develop motors based on impulse-driven higher frequency currents, but didn't manage to turn them into real models.

The next section on impedance effects was short and contained experiments which were conducted by E. Lecher five years earlier. It was followed by a much more significant

section devoted to electrical resonance, providing a precise description of basic elements of a radio system. Tesla talked about resonance as a phenomenon that provides efficient and selective transmission of *"intelligible signals or perhaps even power to any distance without the use of wires."* He added: *"We now know that electric vibration may be transmitted through a single conductor. Why then not try to avail ourselves of the earth for this purpose? We need not be frightened by the idea of distance. To the weary wanderer counting the mileposts the earth may appear very large, but to that happiest of all men, the astronomer, who gazes at the heavens and by their standard judges the magnitude of our globe, it appears very small. And so I think it must seem to the electrician, for when he considers the speed with which the electric disturbance is propagated through the Earth all his idea of distance must completely vanish."* Thinking further about the Earth, as a capacitor with its conducting layer high above the surface, Tesla described an experiment to determine the oscillation period of the Earth's charge. He would connect one end of the generator to the ground and the other to an insulated body of a large surface. He would then change the frequency of the generator and carefully measure voltage of the insulated body, observing potential electric changes at various neighbouring points on the earth's surface. This experiment, if feasible, could give data on the Earth's resonance, but we still do not know whether Tesla tried to do it then or later. The most important part of the lecture is the scheme of the transmitter with one of its terminals connected to an insulated metal body of a large surface and the other terminal connected to the ground, such as to water mains. According to Tesla, the generator would

◀ *Resonant transformer*

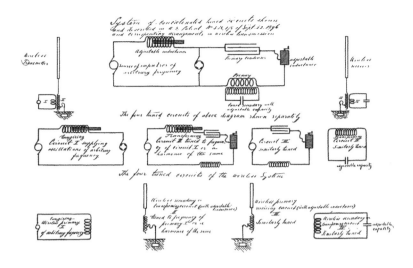

Illustration of a system with four resonant circuits

cause disturbances in the electric charge of the Earth, which could be detected at a distance. To get a sufficiently powerful disturbance, a maximum voltage should be provided at the terminals of the generator. A circuit made of inductance and capacitance, which resonates at the frequency of the generator, would be excited and would detect any disturbance of neighbouring points within a given radius. Several generators could be set to operate in synchronism in which case the vibration could be detected at an arbitrary distance. However, it seems that Tesla did not say everything he knew at that moment, because his possessions revealed a photograph indicating that he had tested a series of various arrangements of

Tesla's coil, illustrating the first step in the evolution
of the magnifying transmitter ▶

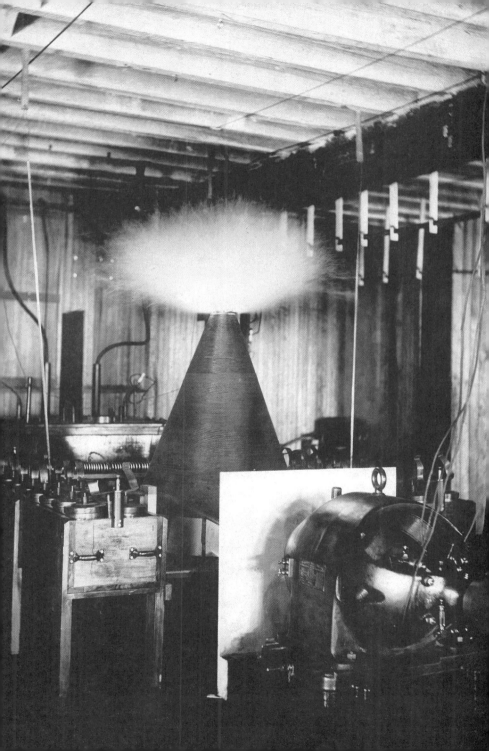

ECTRIC & MANUFAC

COLUMBUS

WESTINGHOUSE
ELECTRIC
&
MANUFACTURING CO
TESLA
POLYPHASE
SYSTEM

inductance and capacitance in the transmission system with a ground connection and an insulated metal body (antenna) in 1892.[29] Furthermore, Tesla did not apply for a patent on the system of antenna and ground connection, which allowed Marconi to be granted a patent on the modified Hertz device in 1895.[30] Marconi replaced the symmetric Hertz's dipole with an asymmetric Tesla type antenna, so his transmitter emitted guided waves as demonstrated in Tesla's scheme, instead of emitting free waves as in Hertz's device.

He would devote the remainder of the lecture to light phenomena produced by various vacuum tubes, interesting experiments with phosphorescent materials in the vacuum, moving on to discuss the atomic structure of the medium surrounding us, the most economical voltage for phosphorescence excitement, and arguing that resonance is the most important natural manifestation of energy. He believed that the collision of atoms, and the state of resonance they achieve after some of these collisions, was the most important effect for the production of light and heat.

Tesla's explanations do not provide actual information about various phenomena but do contain some elements that were later fully explained by modern quantum electronics. For example, the phenomenon that Tesla called resonance of atoms at certain collisions is being used in helium-neon lasers for the excitement of helium atoms in collision with electrons. By virtue of resonant transfer, excited helium atoms transfer energy to unexcited atoms of neon, which emit laser radiation as they return into their base state.

◀   *Tesla's polyphase system at the Columbia Exhibition in 1893*

WORLD'S COLUMBIAN EXHIBITION

That 1893 was an exceptional year for Tesla is further confirmed by his participation in the World's Columbian Exposition – the Chicago World's Fair.[31] In addition to recognizing the 400th anniversary of the discovery of the New World, this fair was especially notable as it was the first in the history of humankind to be illuminated by electric light. The electricity for the illumination was provided by *Westinghouse Electric Company*. For that purpose, Westinghouse made full use of the Tesla polyphase system, which met all energy needs of mechanical facilities and illumination of the whole fair. Tesla was forced to halt his work on radio development to a degree, but he prepared his personal exhibition as a first-class attraction of the fair. *Westinghouse Electric Company* was awarded the contract to provide illumination for the fair beating *General Electric Company* in an open competition. Electricity dominated the whole exhibition. In the period between May and October, the exhibition was visited by about 25 million people, one third of the United States population. Tesla prepared experiments from the field of low frequency currents, demonstrated various motors, showed an experiment with a metal egg spun by the rotating magnetic field, operated his generators of high frequency currents, exposed himself to 1,000,000 volts while leaving people breathless, and used the current flowing through his body to melt wires, turn on bulbs, gas pipes, and run motors. In August, Tesla delivered a lecture at the International Electrical Congress and demonstrated experiments on his electrical and mechanical oscillator. Those were generators with a very stable frequency, which were used to drive chronometers. One of the speakers

Ticket for the World Exhibition in Chicago 1893

at the Congress was T.C. Martin, who wrote the first book on Tesla's work in the electrical engineering field.[26] The Congress was also attended by Professors Helmholtz and Pupin.

POLYPHASE SYSTEM

Polyphase alternating current system was first tested in Colorado Springs in 1891. Nearby a small mining town, Telluride, Westinghouse's engineers built a hydroelectric plant with a polyphase generator. The current was transformed to high voltage and transmitted to the mine where it powered a large synchronous motor.[32]

An industrial exhibition was held in 1891 in Frankfurt, Germany. The most important exhibit was the public application of the Tesla three-phase system. Illumination of the exhibition space and building was provided by electric power transmitted from a hydroelectric plant at Lauffen by a three-phase system at 30,000 V. An alternating current motor of about 2 kW, constructed by Dolivio-Dobrowolsky, was also presented at the exhibition. Visitors gained the impression that it was a discovery that originated in Germany. That was initially reported by an observer of the American Navy, Carl Hering, in the journal *"Electrical World."* The truth was revealed at the following Electrical Congress by Ludwig Gutman, an American electrical engineer, in his paper, *"The Inventor of the Rotary Field System."* He said that everything that was exhibited, including the motor of Dolivio-Dobrowolsky, had been known in the States from 1888, when Tesla demonstrated his polyphase system and applied for many patents on various types of generators, motors and power transmission systems operated by polyphase currents. C.E.L. Brown, the engineer in charge of the construction of the Lauffen-Frankfurt transmission system, including the Dobrowolsky motor, in a letter published in *"Electrical World"* on November 7 1891, stated: "The three phase current as applied at Frankfurt is due to the labors of Mr. Tesla and will be found clearly specified in his patents."[35] After the advent of the Tesla alternating current system, there were others who claimed either that they had made earlier inventions in this field or that they *"improved"* Tesla inventions. Among those, significant place belongs to Galileo Ferraris, a physicist at the University of Turin, who presented a paper on *"Rotazioni elettrodinamiche" (Electrodynamic Rotation)* before the Turin Academy in March 1888. He constructed a model with two orthogonal coils with 90 degrees phase difference in their alternating currents in order to simulate a magnetic field of circularly polarized light. To 'see' the field of circularly polarized wave, Ferraris suspended a metal cylinder on a thread in the alternating current magnetic field. The currents induced by rotating field turned the metal cylinder, and as the thread suspending the cylinder turned, the direction of the cylinder that of a helicoid. It was a nice illustration of circularly polarized light wave, but the model itself had no resemblance to a motor. Later, Ferraris constructed a model that looked like Tesla's asynchronous motor, by placing two coils on the copper cylinder, but such a motor had negligible power. Shortly, Ferraris concluded that such a device could not obtain efficiency above 50%, and his efforts to use iron to that end did not yield any improvements.[33]

As it usually happens, there were those who sought to prove that Tesla was not the original inventor of the polyphase system so they can take advantage of it without paying royalties. It is interesting to mention the destiny of Tesla patents in other countries, in particular in Germany, where he was granted patents similar to those in the U.S. but was subsequently denied, so as not to *"hinder the development of German industry."* A detailed description of these debates can be found in a book by S. Boksan.[33] Following is an excerpt from the ruling on the first group of Tesla's basic patents issued in September 1900 by Judge Townsend of the U.S. District Court for the District of Connecticut:

"It remained to the genius of Nikola Tesla to capture the unruly, unrestrained and hitherto opposing elements in the field of nature and art and to harness them to draw the machines of man. It was he who first showed how to transform the toy of Arago into an engine of power; the 'laboratory experiment' of Bailey into a practically successful motor; he first conceived

the idea that the very impediments of reversal in direction, the contraindications of alternations might be transformed into power-producing rotations, a whirling field of force."[36]

NIAGARA HYDROELECTRIC POWER PLANT

The great potential of Niagara power has always been appealing; however, its power could only be used locally so factories were built next to water turbines. The advances in the field of electricity changed all of this; in 1886, Edward Dean Adams[34], a businessmen and entrepreneur, initiated a bold project to create the first large-scale hydroelectric plant that utilizes the power of the falls, estimated at about 8 million horsepower. The International Niagara Commission was formed, chaired by Lord Kelvin, and a prize of $3,000 was offered for the most practical plan for harnessing the power of the falls. Such a small prize did not attract big companies like *Edison General Electric Company* and *Thomson-Houston Company*, so they did not submit bids. The International Commission received twenty applications during 1890 but rejected all of them. Lord Kelvin favoured the use of direct current, but after the Tesla system had become operational, he acknowledged its supremacy: *"Tesla has contributed more to electrical science than any man up to this time."*

After the failure of the first tender and successful testing of Tesla alternating current system in Telluride and Germany in 1891, the Commission decided that Tesla's hydroelec-

◀ *Nikola Tesla in his forties*

Aerial view of Niagara Falls

tric system should be accepted. Accordingly, the Commission asked in 1893 for new plans and bids from the *Westinghouse Electric Company* and the *General Electric Company*, on a power system consisting of three generating units, each of 5,000 horsepower. Both companies submitted plans to install the Tesla system, as the *General Electric Company*, successor to the *Edison General Electric Company*, had in the meantime secured a license to use Tesla's patents, by various agreements and exchange of patents.

In October 1893, the Commission announced the acceptance of the *Westinghouse Company* proposal for a power plant with a two-phase generator and the *General Electric Company* proposal for a three-phase transmission system. In 1895, the *Westinghouse Company* completed three generators

The inside of the Adams Power Station at Niagara Falls ▶

Name plate on the first generator
at the Niagara Falls power plant

based on thirteen patents, nine of them belonging to Tesla. The first consumer of the produced electricity was *Pittsburgh Reduction Company* for production of aluminium by the Hall process. The next year, the *General Electric Company* completed the transmission and distribution system, which, for the first time in history, transmitted electrical power from Niagara Falls to the city of Buffalo, located 22 miles away.

The most beautiful description of these events was given by Charles Scott, Professor at Yale University, in a memorial review of Nikola Tesla's accomplishments in the field of electrical energy, published in 1943:

"The evolution of electric power from the discovery of Faraday to the initial great installation of the Tesla polyphase system in 1896 is undoubtedly the most tremendous event in all engineering history."[37]

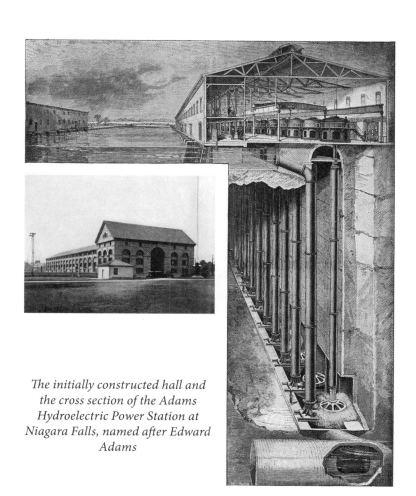

The initially constructed hall and the cross section of the Adams Hydroelectric Power Station at Niagara Falls, named after Edward Adams

Tesla was invited to the commemoration of the Niagara Falls Power Plant inauguration held at the Ellicott Club, Buffalo, on 12 January 1897. In his welcoming address, Tesla enthusiastically described the significance of the event and said:

"We have many a monument of past ages; we have the palaces and pyramids, the temples of Greek and the cathedrals

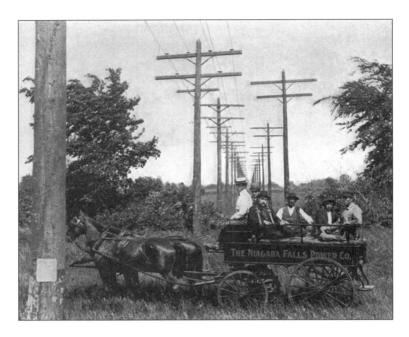

The first transmission line Niagara Falls - Buffalo

of Christendom. In them is exemplified the power of men, the greatness of nations, the love of art and religious devotion. But that monument at Niagara has something of its own, more in accord with our present thoughts and tendencies. It is a monument worthy of our scientific age, a true monument of enlightenment and of peace. It signifies the subjugation of natural forces to the service of man, the discontinuance of barbarous methods, the relieving of millions from want and suffering...

Provided, therefore, that we can avail of currents of sufficiently high tension, a waterfall affords us the most advantageous means of getting power from the Sun sufficient for all our wants, and this recognition has impressed me strongly with

118

the future importance of water power, not so much because of it commercial value, though it may be very great, but chiefly because of its bearing upon our safety and welfare."[38]

Later in the speech, he talked about his new research, and utterly confused everybody by stating that he had found a way to transmit power at a much higher voltage than it was possible with the standard device, and would do it by *"the fulfilment of one of my fondest dreams; namely, the transmission of power from station to station without the employment of any connecting wire!"* He said this at the time when he was preparing his patents on wireless system of power transmission, while the world was only starting to use electricity more widely. In the visitors' book in the Niagara power plant Tesla wrote: *"Final destination New York – with the heart in Niagara.*"[34]

HIGH FREQUENCY AND HIGH VOLTAGE CURRENTS

In the years after 1893 Nikola Tesla worked on the development of his device for high frequency current and wireless transmission of electrical energy. He tested possibilities of applying resonance, crucial for selective transmission of messages in radio technology, allowing simultaneous work of many transmitters and receivers without mutual interference. In an interview published in *"The World"* on 22nd July 894, Tesla announced his plans:

"... I can tell you that I look forward with absolute confidence to sending messages through the Earth without any

wires. I have also great hopes of transmitting electric force in the same way without loss. Concerning the transmission of messages through the Earth I have no hesitation in predicting success..."

Tesla was forced to interrupt his research in the domain of radio and other applications of high frequency currents on 13th March 1895. His laboratory caught fire, destroying all his efforts, equipment, instruments and documents. It was a great tragedy, great material loss and big halt in the development of new and existing inventions. The laboratory had no insurance coverage and was not even in his exclusive ownership.[39]

Many friends came to his rescue, including Mr. Adams, head of the Morgan Group, which had constructed the hydroelectric station at Niagara Falls. Adams invested $40,000 and helped Tesla form a new company. Tesla soon found new premises at 46 East Houston Street, and was ready to start operations in July 1895.[14] Cooperation with the Morgan Group encouraged others to help Tesla and make business arrangements with him.

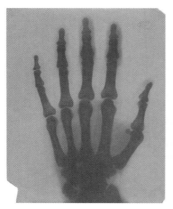 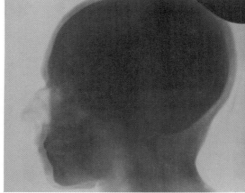

By the end of 1895, Roentgen announced the discovery of x-rays. That discovery inspired many scientists to deal with x-rays, because the research of discharge in rarefied air was extensive. Among those who immediately succeeded were Nikola Tesla and another great inventor of similar origin Mihajlo Pupin. In articles published in March 1896,[40] and later that year, Tesla announced new data about x-rays, which he had earlier classified as "special radiation," and which produced shadowgraph pictures on plates in metal containers. Using his transformer, he easily produced very high voltages and x-rays of high energy. He was the first to notice that those rays caused skin injuries and should be handled carefully. He also constructed several devices with which he obtained excellent shadow photographs at a distance of 10 meters from the source. The following year, he delivered a lecture at the New York Academy of Sciences in which he presented interesting data from his research in this field.[41]

X-ray images generated by Tesla during his experiments

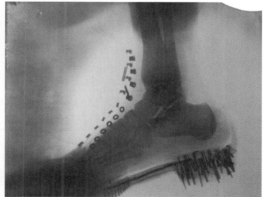

Approximately one year after the fire, Tesla managed to refurbish his laboratory and to continue disrupted research. He worked in a completely new field and had to construct not only new models, but also many auxiliary measurement instruments. He conducted intensive research using transmitters and receivers located within the laboratory, and occasionally experimented with distant receivers set on a ship that navigated the Hudson River. According to Tesla's biography, he managed to obtain transmission over a distance of 26 miles.[14]

In 1897, Tesla completed his research in the field of radio and in September applied for two patents that are the basis of radio technology. One patent is related to a device for transmission of electrical energy (Patent No. 649,621) and the other to the system of transmission of electrical energy (Patent No. 645,576). Those patents included the following new features:

- transmitter with two oscillatory circuits, one of which generates high frequency currents of selected frequency and the other is open, oscillatory antenna circuit consisting of inductance coupled with the primary and capacitance made of elevated metal body (antenna) and grounded metal plate (ground connection);

- receiver with two oscillatory circuits, one of which generates high frequency currents of selected frequencies and the other is open, oscillatory antenna circuit consisting of inductance coupled with the primary and capacitance made of elevated metal body (antenna) and grounded metal plate (ground connection);

Such a wireless transmission system is able to select only waves of a particular wavelength from the spectrum of electromagnetic waves, while suppressing other signals in the re-

Instrument for the reception of radio-waves, 1896-1899.
Tesla used similar instruments since 1892.

ceiving circuit. Resonance contributes to the sensitivity of the receiver, because of a better adjustment between the source of electromagnetic waves (transmitter) and the open oscillatory circuit of the receiver. Similarly, transmission from the adjusted antenna circuit provides a maximum antenna current and thus, a maximum transmission. Dimensions and shape of the antenna also influence the overall efficiency of the transmission; however, Tesla's patents do not contain any precise instructions related to antennas.

A year earlier, Marconi applied in England for a patent on a modified Hertz device, by replacing Hertz symmetric radiator with Tesla open antenna circuit.[42] However, as Marconi used Hertz's technique of excitement and set the spark gap directly between the terminals of the antenna and ground connection, his transmitter produced undetermined oscillations, that is, oscillations dependant on the length and type of the elevated body and ground connection. Also, the ordinary spark gap oscillator gave a small number of exciting impulses per second and, given the relatively high frequency of the currents generated in Marconi's antenna, created short impulses which abruptly diminished. It is practically impossible to know the frequency of a transmitter in such a system: its spectrum is complex, and the transmitter cannot be "adjusted" by resonance. Marconi achieved some success with a sensitive device for detection of weak impulses of high frequency current, as well as with an accidental discovery that he had not thought to be important. Namely, the elevation of antenna reduces the spectrum of frequencies of antenna currents and Marconi empirically established that the receiver distance increases. In a similar way, he increased the height of receiving antenna and experimentally found the most favourable conditions for the transmission and reception of longer waves. He finally understood the essence of Tesla's approach: to generate high frequency currents of a certain frequency and then feed the signal to the antenna. Marconi adopted Tesla's solution for transmitter and achieved successful transmission of the first radio signals across the Atlantic in 1901.[43] He did not mention Tesla's name and was even granted a U.S. patent, which was invalidated many years later, when the U.S. Supreme Court in its decision rendered in June 1943, decided that the Marconi's Patent No. 763,772 had not contained anything above and beyond that was included in existing patents of Tesla, Stone and Lodge.[45]

In 1896, Lloyds of London suggested that Tesla should set up a wireless system to broadcast the international yacht race, from boats to shore. Tesla's assistant Scherff advised him to accept the job and use it to establish a company for the promotion of message transmission through his wireless system. Tesla did not accept, expecting to make fortune out of his invention, which, unfortunately, never happened.

In 1898, Tesla decided to publicly demonstrate the radio system in his way, originally and attractively. He constructed a model of a boat that he operated by remote control, using radio impulses.[46] The model boat was demonstrated in a large pool in the great hall of Madison Square Garden in September 1898, during the First Annual Electrical Exhibition. It was a sensational demonstration; however, many did not grasp the essence of the invention. According to Tesla, that was the first robot, a representative of the new category of machines that would be helpful to humans in a new way, as he described in an article published by the "Century":

"The automatons so far constructed had "borrowed minds," so to say, as each formed merely part of the distant operator who conveyed to it his intelligent orders; but this art is only in the beginning. I purpose to show that, however impossible it may now seem, an automaton may be contrived which will have its "own mind," and by this I mean that it will be able, independently of any operator, left entirely to itself, to perform, in response to external influences affecting its sensitive organs, a great variety of acts and operations as if it had intelligence.

It will be able to follow a course laid out or to obey orders given far in advance; it will be capable of distinguishing between what it ought and ought not to do, and of making experiences or, otherwise stated, of recording impressions which will definitely affect its subsequent actions. In fact I have already conceived such a plan..."[47]

The above description could have been written recently, rather than a century ago. It is easy to understand how difficult it was for his contemporaries to comprehend such visionary ideas, at the time when there was no radio, and electricity

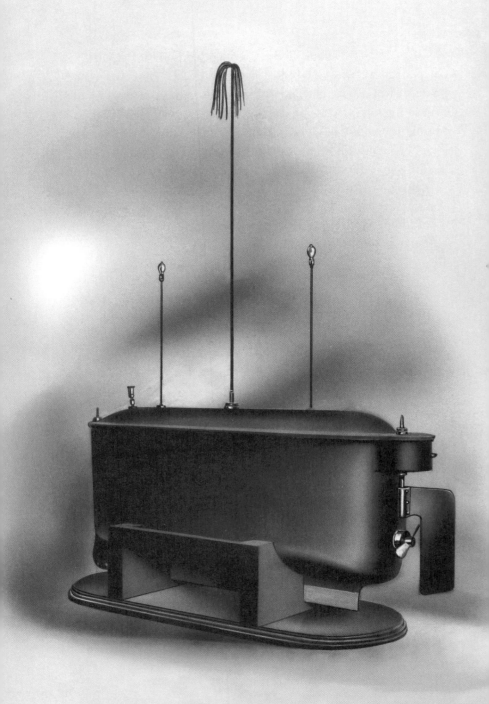

was a fledgling science. Nowadays, similar statements would sound realistic, because many of Tesla's hypotheses have been brought to life by the help of computers and complex electronic devices. Tesla's genius and vision created a small masterpiece of engineering by pulling together basic electrical engineering principles, Tesla's data transmission radio, and various motors and relays to create this remote-controlled model boat. Tesla used a series of radio transmitted impulses to control the boat's engine, directing it forward and backward, left and right, and controlling its speed. His patent described a simple version of a receiver containing an antenna, a coherer, a primary relay circuit and batteries. As an impulse was received, the coherer would reduce its resistance and switch on the primary relay. The primary relay would switch on the battery powering the secondary relay which would activate a clock mechanism, turning the coherer for 180 degrees, bringing it back into the low conductance state and making it ready to receive and process another impulse. A combination of precise mechanics and electrical relays were used to propagate the effect of an impulse through the electrical circuits which controlled the behaviour of the main and ancillary electrical motors that controlled the movements of the boat. It is surprising how reliable was such a relatively complex system. It was fairly slow, indeed, however controlling a model boat did not require instant response. Tesla had patented this invention in several countries, but it was so much ahead of its time, that he couldn't find anyone who expressed an intent to commercialize it. There was little understanding for

◄ *Tesla's model boat with wireless remote control demonstrated at the Maddison Square Garden in 1898*

Tesla's explanations of the potential of such devices, backed by demonstrations of two models he had constructed and publicly demonstrated, neither for Tesla's assertions that such devices will be very useful for defence against submarines or flying machines (still non-existent). So great was the disbelief in the feasibility of this invention that one of the patents was only granted after the main examiner of the Patent Office witnessed the operation of the model and was persuaded that the concept stated in the patent application was feasible.

Tesla said that he had been working on the application of radio waves for remote control since 1893, when he published the design of his basic radio. For the model demonstrated in 1898, which he had constructed the previous year, he applied a special technique with secure message transmission. Although we cannot be certain, it is most likely that he used dual-wavelength selective transmitters and receivers, that were extremely resistant to interferences, which he described in his Colorado Springs Notes[48] and patented in 1900 (Patent No. 613,809).

WIRELESS TRANSMISSION
OF ENERGY

In addition to the research of low-power wireless signal transmission, Tesla spent significant effort in attempts to transmit high-power energy wirelessly. He believed that for such an application, high or extremely high voltage currents were necessary; a hypothesis based on the observation that losses decrease with the increase of voltage and the reduction of current, resulting in conductivity to increase while maintaining the same power level. High and extremely high voltages are easily produced by high frequency currents, so Tesla's thinking was that by using extremely high voltages, the transmission line could become wireless. According to Tesla, a variant of wireless transmission from 1897 (Patent No. 645,57649) functions in the following manner: a generator is connected to the Tesla transformer's secondary coil, whose length is approximately one-quarter of the wavelength of the alternating current in the circuit. The secondary coil leads into an open oscillatory circuit consisting of an insulated metal body suspended in air (antenna) and a conducting grounded body (ground connection). Granting this patent required the demonstration of an experiment in front of the main examiner of the Patent Office. There is a photograph that shows the experiment in question. The end of the transmitter's antenna is connected to a glass tube from which air was extracted to create the pressure approximately equal to the pressure of atmosphere at the height of ten kilometres above the Earth. The other end of the tube is in a similar way connected to the terminal of the receiver's antenna, and energy from the primary coil of the receiving transformer is conveyed to the secondary coil of the low voltage receiver. Tesla "simulated" transmission of the energy through the Earth's and a rarefied atmosphere, some sort of two-conductor system similar to the one described in an earlier patent where he used a thin wire as a conductor of power line (Patent No. 593,138)[50]. The other conductor in that system is again the Earth, connected with transmitting and receiving transformers through grounded metal plates.

Realizing that the requirement for a several kilometre-high antenna was unrealistic, instead of going into height,

he envisaged using even higher voltages (100 million Volts) and believed that wireless transmission of energy could be achieved with a moderately elevated insulated body with a large diameter sphere. Apparently, Tesla fully believed that his system *"disturbs the electric charge of the earth"* which was the basis of his hypothesis for wireless transmission of energy. In a way typical of him, he denied the existence of any similarity between the transmission of electromagnetic waves in his system and in the Hertz device, which only emits electromagnetic radiation into the open space. As Tesla wanted to achieve directional transmission, the energy emitted through an antenna using a Hertz device would simply be lost in space. In his Long Island Notes[51], he even used Hertz's formulae to determine optimal frequencies for an antenna system consisting of the Earth and an elevated insulated body, so as to minimize radiation and determined that the solution was to use alternating currents of only several tens of Hertz. It is well known that Tesla, from the beginning of his research on radio, insisted on much lower frequencies than those used by Hertz, so that the Earth could be used as one of the conductors. Tesla certainly could not have known the complete theory of radio wave transmission, but he correctly felt that lower frequencies need to be used in order to avoid emitting energy into the space and direct them through Earth's surface, on which Tesla insisted in order to obtain economical transmission over large distances. When it comes to the selection of frequencies, Tesla has correctly asserted that lower frequency waves would be better "tied" to the Earth's surface, although

◄   *An experiment that illustrates supply of electrical energy using a single wire utilising earth as the second conductor* his general view of the problem of transmission was not correct. He was right in imagining that there are oscillations in the Earth's crust, but always in combination with the electromagnetic wave that surrounds the space around the Earth. Tesla's view of transmission was too simple for this complex phenomenon, but it is still fascinating that even with such a model he introduced concepts such as the Earth's resonance and standing waves, and derived an accurate calculation of Earth's resonant frequency (Patent No. 787,412)[52].

Experiments with high voltages became dangerous for Tesla and so he decided to build a new laboratory where he could produce voltages above four million volts, as he did previously in his New York laboratory in Houston Street. However, he had no funds for a new laboratory, so started searching for sponsors. As noted previously, in 1896 he rejected an excellent offer to establish a wireless transmission service because he considered it to be insignificant in comparison to the fortune he thought awaited him.

COLORADO SPRINGS LABORATORY

When Leonard E. Curtis, a member of the electric society from Colorado Springs, heard that Tesla wanted to open a new laboratory, he suggested that it could be built on his estate in Colorado Springs where he could obtain the electrical energy he needed. He would receive financial aid from John Jacob Astor, the owner of the Waldorf Astoria Hotel, where Tesla often stayed. With $30,000, Tesla built the laboratory and filled it with new instruments and equipment.[48] In a shed of approximately 30 by 30 m in dimension, in the middle of the space stood Tesla's transformer with a primary coil of 15m in diameter. The space was filled with coils, capacitors made as battery of bottles with saline solution, both on the inner and outer sides (capacitor electrodes), transformers, switches, fuses, etc. In the middle of the shed, the roof construction was left open leaving space for a large antenna post with a metal ball on top that was protruding through the roof high above the building. Tesla was changing iteratively the shape of the secondary coil of his high frequency transformer from a cone to a cylinder, while maintaining the same size of the primary coil; finally, he added a third coil, called "the extra coil."

Tesla kept a diary of his research in Colorado Springs, which began on June 1, 1899 and ended on January 7, 1900. The diary contains 507 pages of writing and 193 pages of drawings.[48] In the last phase of the experimental work, Tesla, took many photographs of which 63 are published in this book, and 40 are stored in the archives at the Museum of Nikola Tesla in Belgrade. Before coming to Colorado Springs, Tesla described his largest high frequency spark oscillator in his patent "Device for Transmission of Electrical Energy" applied in 1897.[49] High frequency transformer of this oscillator had a flat spiral shaped secondary coil with 50 turns of wire 2.9 mm in diameter, and a primary coil consisting of a single turn of very thick wire 244 cm in diameter. The working frequency of the oscillator was around 240 kHz. In Colorado Springs, Tesla built a considerably larger oscillator. In a later article he stated that he wished to perfect the method of individualisation and isolation of energy transmission, as well as to prove the laws of propagation of energy through the ground and atmosphere.[48]

According to his press statements in that period, Tesla had the intent to transmit radio signals to Paris during the following year (1900). Concluding from his statement to the United States Patent Office in 1902, it seems that he had an even more ambitious target:

"I wished to prove the best conditions in which the transmitter can be used to transfer a signal across the Atlantic and Pacific oceans, as well as to perfect all the details of my system before I get into the commercial business. In other words, although if you ask me, I had no doubt in the possibility of that sort of transmission considering the experiments and measurements I accomplished in New York, I wanted to be sure that not only can I transfer messages but my undertaking would be a commercial success."[53]

In November 1900, the press had written that Tesla was quickly progressing with the completion of his system and that the messages he would send could not be interfered.

By analysing Tesla's diary, it was evident that Tesla spent most of his time on the transmitter (56%), and the receiver (21%), followed by measuring the antenna capacity (16%) and all the other investigations and examinations (6%).

In its initial phase, the transmitter - spark oscillator, had a typical shape of Tesla's high frequency oscillator with a tightly coupled primary and secondary coil (around 0.6%). The high frequency transformer was wound in a cone shape with the middle diameter of over 12 m. In its final design, the transformer had 29 turns in the secondary coil and one or two turns in the primary coil. The primary coil was wound with a multiple wire cable and the secondary coil with a stan-

◀ *Colorado Springs Laboratory*

dard circularly shaped wire. Coils had to be very large due to high voltages he was planning to work with.

Early on in his research at Colorado Springs, Tesla had altered the construction of his oscillator by adding an "extra coil" connected to the secondary coil, which he used on a regular basis thereafter. According to Tesla, this coil made it possible to obtain higher voltages compared to his classical oscillator. In fact, this coil changes the operating regime of the spark oscillator turning it into a system with three resonant circuits and three resonant frequencies.[54] In a later phase, Tesla changed the shape of the secondary coil of the high frequency oscillator and applied a system with a cylindrical coils of 15 m diameter. The coupling of primary and secondary coils was again strong. In the middle of the high frequency transformer, the "extra" coil was placed concentrically, weakly coupled with the primary and secondary coils. Tesla used glass bottles to make the capacitors of the primary circuit; electrodes were connected into a bottle filled with a mixture of salt and water, acting as a dielectric of a capacitor battery.

While designing system components, Tesla calculated coil inductances, needed capacitance, the frequency of the

spark breaker, and the mutual induction of the transformer coils. Calculations were done using a simple Thomson formula and other formulae he used from literature. He would experimentally check all estimated values by making measurements using a limited set of measurement devices available at that time. Parasitic capacitance of the secondary coil was one of the side-effects causing issues during measurements. Tesla came up with a technique of winding coils in a way that reduces the parasitic capacitance. He believed, accurately, that the highest voltage would be obtained when the parasitic capacitance is the smallest. After studying his notes, we can recognize the insight and intuition that helped him resolve a completely new set of problems related to a technique that was just being born. Most interesting was his assertion that the length of the secondary coil's wire should be a quarter of the wavelength of the transmitter's operating frequency. Such an assumption was in contradiction with the simplified theory of tightly coupled resonant circuits at the time. This assertion has been confirmed only recently, through scientific

Tesla's transformer operating with a third "extra"
coil added to the transformer

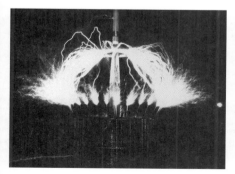 

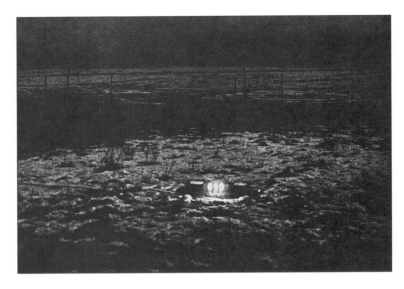

An experiment that illustrates induction effects of a high-power electrical oscillator

papers describing the secondary coil as a helicoid resonator [55]. Further research in this area has confirmed Tesla's assumption on the optimal length of the wire for certain ratios of lengths and diameters of the coil, which is yet another confirmation of his intuition and originality in resolving problems that no-one had answered before.

By developing measurements of frequencies and high voltages, Tesla was able to confirm his theoretical assumptions. He determined the moment of resonance by the length of the sparks, or by the light bulb illumination that was coupled inductively with the oscillator coil. He measured the voltage by the length of the spark between the metal spheres in the same way results are obtained when working with direct currents.

Tesla dedicated a lot of his time in Colorado Springs to examining the receiver with sensitive devices - coherers. During his stay there, he produced four patents on receivers that used the "method of accumulation" (we are only referring to the patents he was awarded). Considering that some patents were presented at the beginning of his stay, and the other two only came about from the dividing of the first two, it is clear that they are inventions from the New York laboratory. The improvements that he made in Colorado Springs were a continuation and elaboration of his earlier work. In his notes, there are around one hundred different interconnection layouts of sensitive devices in which he used methods of accumulation with feedback to switch on the sensitive device promptly upon receiving the signal.[56] Additionally, he designed several types of receivers that utilized thermal effects produced by high frequency currents.

Tesla experimented with the monopole antenna, a metal sphere at the top of the post, for a full month. This was a small antenna in relation to the operating wavelength, and the measurements were in fact reduced to the measurements of small capacitances. As a theoretical model he used the formula for calculating static capacity of an ellipsoidal vertical wire in vicinity of a metal board. Interesting was his observation a precise values cannot be obtained with high frequencies because of the difference in the "static" and "dynamic" capacity. His measurements of capacitances were meticulously accurate, to the order of picofarads!

Tesla's diary of the research conducted at Colorado Springs illustrates the method of a scientist who combined theoretical and experimental investigations in an iterative manner, until reaching a desired outcome. However, as in every research, Tesla would on occasion face unexpected prob-

Colorado Springs Laboratory

lems, which he would examine carefully in order to reach a correct explanation. As an example, Tesla observed fire balls appearing among the huge sparks between the terminal of his high frequency transformer and the ground. He gave a possible theoretical explanation of this phenomenon that still remains a partial mystery to this day. Research of this type wasn't necessarily planed, but as Tesla said, he conducted it "*from purely scientific interests of the time.*"

Tesla was a meticulous observer, so his diary captures not only purely scientific facts, but also descriptions of the laboratory site and its surroundings, as well as the impact of weather on his experiments.

LONG ISLAND LABORATORY

Tesla returned to New York from Colorado Springs in January 1900.

His epic experiments at Colorado Springs left a lasting impact on Tesla which he shared with his closest friends, including R.U. Johnson who persuaded him to write an article about his research for "The Century Magazine." Johnson was one of the editors of the magazine and Tesla's good friend. He lived with his family on Madison Avenue, a wealthy area of New York, which Tesla often visited. Their lasting friendship is evidenced in the saved correspondence between Tesla and Mr. & Mrs. Johnson who, in particular, admired this great man.

Tesla wrote an article that was rereferred back twice with requests for modifications. The name of the article was unusual, "The Problem of Increasing Human Energy."[47] Instead of presenting a scientific explanation of his work, Tesla described a philosophical system in an original way typical of him, arguing that the progress of humanity can be viewed as a mechanical process, instigated and controlled by the available energy; this article went through a number of iterations but remained highly unusual and often cited.

Tesla presented the first version of his article to Mr. Johnson in late January 1900, at a festive dinner arranged by the Johnsons family for that occasion. The article failed to impress Mr. Johnson, who expected it to describe Tesla's system of wireless transmission of electrical energy in 4000 words, ready for release in March or April issue of the "Century" magazine. Having read the introduction and the three main chapters, Johnson said that the article contained a pile

Long Island Plant with the "World System"
transmission tower in construction

of cold philosophical stones instead of hot, digestible facts. Mr. Johnson suggested the article to be extended, which Tesla wholeheartedly accepted. Instead of four, the article contained sixteen chapters in the end, and was handed in for the third time at the end of March.

In the final version, Tesla dedicated more attention to the philosophical side of the problem and changed the title from "The Problem of Transmitting Energy" to "The Problem of Increasing Human Energy". In later re-prints the title was extended further: "With Special Retrospect to the Use of Energy of the Sun."

Tesla begins by introducing the concept of "human mass" and the forces that move this mass. *"Conceive, then, man as a mass urged on by a force. This mass is impelled in one direction by a force f, which is resisted by another partly frictional and partly negative force R, acting in a direction exactly opposite, and retarding the movement of the mass. Man, however, is not an ordinary mass, consisting of spinning atoms and molecules, and containing merely heat-energy. He is a mass possessed of certain higher qualities by reason of the creative principle of life with which he is endowed. What is most wonderful of all, he is capable of increasing or diminishing his velocity of movement by the mysterious power he possesses of appropriating more or less energy from other substance, and turning it into motive energy."*

He then moves on to introduce the concept of Human Energy: *"The human energy will then be given by the product $\frac{1}{2} MV^2 = \frac{1}{2} MV \times V$, in which M is the total mass of man in the ordinary interpretation of the term "mass," and V is a certain hypothetical velocity, which, in the present state of science, we are unable exactly to define and determine. To increase the human energy is, therefore, equivalent to increasing this product, and there are, as will readily be seen, only three ways possible to attain this result."* The first way, argues Tesla, is to increase the mass, the second way is to reduce the impeding, negative forces (thus increasing the velocity), and the third way is to increase the impelling force (which likewise increases velocity). He further develops his thinking and comes to an answer to the core existential problems: *"So we find that the three possible solutions of the great problem of increasing human energy are answered by the three words: food, peace, work. These three words sound the key-notes of the Christian religion. Their sci-*

Interior of the Long Island Plant, summer 1902

entific meaning and purpose now clear to me: food to increase the mass, peace to diminish the retarding force, and work to increase the force accelerating human movement. These are the only three solutions which are possible of that great problem, and all of them have one object, one end, namely, to increase human energy." The remainder of the article elaborates these three solutions with such imagination, vision, and goodness, worthy of the greatest minds humankind has seen.

(1) How can the human mass be increased? "*The mass will be increased by careful attention to health, by substantial food,*

by moderation, by regularity of habits, by promotion of marriage, by conscientious attention to the children, and, generally stated, by the observance of all the many precepts and laws of religion and hygiene. Conversely, it scarcely need be stated that everything that is against the teachings of religion and the laws of hygiene is tending to decrease the mass. Whisky, wine, tea, coffee, tobacco, and other such stimulants are responsible for the shortening of the lives of many, and ought to be used with moderation. But I do not think that rigorous measures of suppression of habits followed through many generations are commendable. It is wiser to preach moderation than abstinence." Tesla further emphasizes the importance of clean water and advocates vegetarianism as *"every effort should be made to stop the wanton and cruel slaughter of animals, which must be destructive to our morals. To free ourselves from animal instincts and appetites, which keep us down, we should begin at the very root from which we spring: we should effect a radical reform in the character of the food."* He closes this section with his research on ozone and nitrogen oxidation that could prove useful in the production of artificial fertilisers used in agriculture. This was the first time in the article that he mentioned the impact of high frequency currents generated by his high frequency transformer, which *"burn nitrogen from the atmosphere"*, as demonstrated by sample photographs from his Colorado Springs laboratory.

(2) How can the velocity of human mass be increased by reducing negative forces that impede velocity? Eliminate ignorance and wars, Tesla says. Occurrence of wars, he argues, could be reduced over time by decreasing the number of people who participate in wars, achieved through development of automated combat machines that will over time be

"controlled by only a few people...The loss of lives will become gradually smaller, until finally, with a constant decrease of individuals, only machines will encounter each other in the competition, without bloodshed, and people will only be interested, ambitious spectators." He mentions his invention, the remotely controlled boat, as an example of a machine that could be controlled by a few people from vast distances. Tesla's boat is a cornerstone of the wireless remote control technology (Tesla used the term Teleautomatics), extensively used today for land, sea, and airborne vehicles. He further stretches his vision of robots and artificial intelligence that is becoming a reality today, 120 years after the article was written: *"I purpose to show that, however impossible it may now seem, an automaton may be contrived which will have its "own mind," and by*

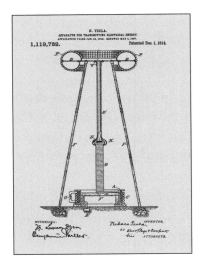

Tesla's high-voltage transformer (Pat br. 1.119.732)
and the antenna tower at Long Island

this I mean that it will be able, independent of any operator, left entirely to itself, to perform, in response to external influences affecting its sensitive organs, a great variety of acts and operations as if it had intelligence."

(3) How can the velocity of human mass be increased by increasing the force that accelerates it? "Harness the Sun's energy", Tesla says. *"Of the three possible solutions of the main problem of increasing human energy, this is by far the most important to consider, not only because of its intrinsic significance, but also because of its intimate bearing on all the many elements and conditions which determine the movement of humanity."*

He mentions three ways of drawing energy from the sun: releasing it from the burning material, such as coal, wood, oil; capturing it from the ambient and atmosphere, such as wind and water; and finally, transferring it from one place to another. He elaborates in detail the production and use of materials such as iron, aluminium, copper, and expresses his views on the economical gains that could be achieved by using less energy in their production. Similar are his thoughts on enhancing or even transforming the ways energy is released from coal, "for ultimately we must succeed in obtaining electricity from coal in a more direct way, involving no great loss of heat-energy. Whether coal can be oxidized by a cold process is still a question. Its combination with oxygen always evolves heat, and whether the energy of the combination of the carbon with another element can be turned directly into electrical energy has not yet been determined." An entire section is devoted to obtaining energy from renewable sources such as wind and son, although Tesla could not envisage the progress made in solar cell technology a hundred and twenty years later, Nevertheless, his thoughts and his vision were immensely close to the burning ecological themes so prevalent today.

In the last chapter of his article, Tesla progressed from wireless telecommunication, such as intercontinental wireless telegraph, further into his vision of wireless transmission of energy. "The most valuable observation made in the course of these investigations was the extraordinary behaviour of the atmosphere toward electric impulses of excessive electromotive force. The experiments showed that the air at the ordinary pressure became distinctly conducting, and this opened up the wonderful prospect of transmitting large amounts of electrical energy for industrial purposes to great distances without wires, a possibility which, up to that time, was thought of only as a scientific dream. His ideas of wireless transmission of electrical energy, first through one wire, and then through the ground, were backed by experiments from his Colorado Springs laboratory; however, Tesla never managed to transmit a sizeable power wirelessly. At that time, the transmission of electrical waves had still been explained through analogies with mechanical engineering, which wasn't fully accepted even at that time, only to be completely abandoned later. Unfortunately, Tesla's experiments at Colorado Springs, and later at his new laboratory at Long Island, did not prove his vision, and it remains that way to the present day. According to Tesla, wireless transmission of energy would enable the transfer of required energy for illumination and other needs to any part of the world; however, we never found any proof that something like this was possible. Wireless transmission of electrical energy is widely in use today, but only for relatively small signals in the system of global telecommunications.

"The Problem with Increasing Human Energy" was such a unique scientific article that had no similarities with typical scientific works presenting technical achievements that were written at the time, or even today. Scientific research was conducted in a different way at the turn of the twentieth century compared to today. Computers have added great value in all fields of scientific research through their ability to simulate a huge number of variations without having to conduct physical experiments. The electrical engineering profession was only emerging with Tesla being one of the founders in the fields of high-power electrical engineering, robotics, radio, and applied mechanical engineering. Tesla's imagination and broad thinking naturally took him beyond the field of engineering into philosophy, sociology, and religion where he offered insights that feel incredibly relevant 120 years after they were written.

The article stirred many minds, among which was J. Pierpont Morgan, an American financier who, with $150,000, financially assisted Tesla with his next big project in building the world's radio-station on an island near New York. Morgan already participated in the exploration of Tesla's inventions in the polyphase electricity area, as one of the prime investors in the Niagara Falls Power Company.

Tesla began to bring out his ideas of a World Radio station that will transmit signals over the Atlantic with a lot of enthusiasm and excitement. The money he received was not enough to bring his grand idea to life completely, but he began working hoping to receive further funding, as we can conclude from the extensive correspondence between Tesla and Morgan. To some degree, Tesla wrongfully assumed that Morgan was helping him for non-commercial reasons; however, it appears that Morgan main objective was to take control of radio technology, for which, at one point, Tesla did not have a rival.

Tesla located his radio station on Long Island, 60 miles away from New York. Tesla's friend Stanford White, a well-known architect, who created a number of churches and large edifices, agreed to work out the preliminary estimates for the main and tower buildings. Tesla required a 154 ft (about 50 m) high tower with a large copper ball of 100 ft diameter fitted on the top. The challenging construction of the tower was designed by V.D Crow, one of White's colleagues who later became well-known as a designer of hospitals and public buildings.

During construction, Tesla's tower had changed compared to its original design, ending up as wooden tower with a hemispheric top of unusual beauty. The tower was finished in 1902 and occupied an area of almost 900 square meters including the main building.

The entire laboratory equipment was made on Tesla's special orders. He worked alongside the builders and engineers, making sure that everything gets ready for his future experiments. He was tireless and expected the same of his co-workers, however treating them well and rewarding overtime work.

In order to explain the purpose of his forthcoming research, Tesla published a brochure describing his new "World System."[57] power plant. In the introduction, he said that *"the World System is the result of a combination of a couple of different discoveries that the researcher came across in the course of his other investigations and numerous views."* Most fascinating is his 12-point summary of the vast number of applications that his new World System could eventually offer:

1. *The inter-connection of the existing telegraph exchanges or offices all over the world;*

2. *The establishment of a secret and non-interferable government telegraph service;*

3. *The inter-connection of all the present telephone exchanges or offices on the Globe;*

4. *The universal distribution of general news, by telegraph or telephone, in connection with the Press;*

5. *The establishment of such a 'World-System' of intelligence transmission for exclusive private use;*

6. *The inter-connection and operation of all stock tickers of the world;*

7. *The establishment of a 'World-System' of musical distribution, etc.;*

8. *The universal registration of time by cheap clocks indicating the hour with astronomical precision and requiring no attention whatever;*

9. *The world transmission of typed or handwritten characters, letters, checks, etc.;*

10. *The establishment of a universal marine service enabling the navigators of all ships to steer perfectly without compass, to determine the exact location, hour and speed, to prevent collisions and disasters, etc.;*

11. *The inauguration of a system of world-printing on land and sea;*

12. *The world reproduction of photographic pictures and all kinds of drawings or records.*

Tesla's predictions came to life over the next one hundred years; however, in those days, most of Tesla's ideas seemed like

Tesla's high-voltage transformer in operation

fantasies. When he told journalists that, in the future, every person will have a small transceiver used to communicate with other users of the system, journalists mocked him. In those days, the radio was only used for point-to-point communication, but Tesla had foreseen how the wireless radio technology would evolve into a complex system for broadcasting news, music, letters, payments, etc. He went further to describe possible applications in marine navigation, stock market exchange, and distribution of accurate time signals globally.

Tesla's notes from the Long Island laboratory contain a number of incomplete ideas including possibilities of television picture transmission. Inspired by the human eye, Tesla came up with the idea of transmitting elements of the picture through high frequency currents which are combined into a single "nerve" i.e. a wire that transmits them in parallel." These ideas had some similarities with the way television evolved, particularly related to spreading the picture into elements, but its evolution followed a different path, utilising photoelectric tubes

Tesla kept writing notes of his investigations at Long Island for a couple of years; however, they were not as neat and tidy as those written at Colorado Springs. He had to battle with a lot more challenges, notably finances which turned out to be a huge problem that distracted him from focusing on the design of his World System. He neglected the fact that the money was running out while the end of his project still remained elusive. Around 1905, his mounting debt got him into the court resulting in closure of his Long Island laboratory. Tesla's tower was never completed and most of the equipment had been taken by bailiffs. He returned to New York, opened his new office at 165 Broadway, and managed to win some financial support which enabled him to return most of his debt, but wasn't sufficient to resurrect lab work.

Tesla's key financier in those days was J.P. Morgan who funded the initial setup of the World System at Long Island. It transpires that Tesla and Morgan fell out on the purpose of the 'World Station'; Tesla saw it as the means to develop a system for world-wide energy transmission, whereas Morgan expected a world-wide wireless system for signal transmission. Once Morgan realised that Tesla system is trying to deliver something different, his enthusiasm for further funding faded away. In numerous letters, Tesla was trying to convince Morgan that transmission of signals would be a small achievement compared to his grand vision of energy transmission, but it was in vain. Roughly at the same time, in 1901, Marconi demonstrated wireless transmission of ship-to-shore telegraph signal, which attracted significant media coverage. Back in 1896, Tesla had a chance to achieve something similar, if not more impressive, but he was possessed by his grand vision of wireless energy transmission and neglected huge opportunities in the evolution of wireless signal transmission. Whatever the case, Morgan pulled off, other potential investors followed, leaving Tesla with no finances; sadly, further work on his World System has been abandoned before it was completed, never to be resurrected.

John O'Neal, who knew Tesla in person and collected numerous artefacts on Tesla's life and work said the following about Tesla's inability to deal with business matters: *"If Tesla could have tolerated a business manager, and had placed the development of his patents in the hands of a business-man, he could have established as early as 1896 a practical ship-to-shore, and probably a trans-oceanic wireless service; and these would have given him a monopoly in the field".* [14]

Tesla's accountant and secretary George Scherff tried to convince Tesla to let him manage the licencing of many Tesla's patents that others used without paying any royalties. Persuasions did not help, because Tesla kept repeating that those were all small matters and that millions would come soon. Millions never came, but Scherff stayed with him up until the closure of the laboratory at Wardencliff. Tesla could not pay him anymore, but he would still come once a week to take care of Tesla's finances and papers. Tesla prudently paid for the services he used but could not bother to check if he had sufficient funds.

TESLA'S LESSER KNOWN INVENTIONS IN THE FIELD OF RADIO TRANSMISSION

Although Tesla had remarkable ideas in the field of radio technology, he considered that transmission of messages wasn't as important as transmission of energy and consequently he missed the opportunity to contribute in the next phase of radio development when the ideas of his "World Radio Station" started to become reality. His patent number 685,973[59] is a good example of what he considered as a "less" important invention. It describes a method of intensifying signal transmission by devising a receiver that accumulates series of multiple selective impulses that charge a capacitor resulting in an amplified signal with an increased signal-to-noise ratio. This method was "rediscovered" in later years and used for the purpose of increasing the signal-to-noise ratio. In fact, Tesla wanted to maximize the level of the incoming signal by rectifying the high frequency signal and charging the capacitor that is periodically connected to receiving device, so that the accumulated effect of the receiving device would be above the ones that the individual impulses could produce. Receivers based on these principles are used today to suppress noise and maximize signal-to-noise ratio.

Another important invention, which increases message throughout and reduces interference, is Tesla's receiver that sends radio signals on two (or more) radio frequencies simultaneously.[60] As a result, the interference between signals operating on different frequencies is significantly reduced, as well as the likelihood that disturbances affecting one signal can have an impact on the other signal. Tesla had predicted that use of multiple frequencies would further eliminate mutual adverse impacts. Additionally, this type of signal transmission can increase message security by dropping out occasional signal impulses which makes them illegible to a potential eavesdropper that may be listening on the same frequency but does not possess the same impulse pattern to decode the message.

Tesla described these types of receivers and transmitters in patent no 725.605, which were never applied, to our knowledge. More recently, Tesla's transmission principle has been 're-invented' as the "spread-spectrum" communication system. Modern transceivers of this type are typically used in defence applications, as the level of encryption achieved by applying double modulation of multiple frequency signals is extremely difficult to decipher. Modern electronics applies these communication principles in a much more effective way than it was possible in Tesla's time. Sadly, Tesla's name is not associated with this invention as contemporary scientists had not contemplated to verify patents going back as far as the beginning of the twentieth century.

NEW FIELDS OF WORK AND TESLA'S VISIONS

When he realized that further efforts with the World Radio Station are futile in absence of proper funding, Tesla returned to some of his old ideas in the field of mechanical engineering. Around 1896 Tesla developed mechanical oscillators (Patents 514,169 and 517,900), which he applied to generate high frequency currents with very high accuracy (Patent 511,916). The working frequency of a mechanical generator would change slightly as the load varies, making it impossible to derive accurate time from alternate currents. To overcome this fluctuation, Tesla invented a mechanism that regulates the frequency depending on mechanical vibrations taking into account mechanical parameters (mass and elasticity), as well as electrical parameters (inductance and capacitance), in order to maintain a stable working frequency. Somewhat unusual were his experiments with mechanical vibrations, to the extent of causing distress and some damage to the neighbouring buildings. According to Tesla's first biographer John O'Neil, Tesla attached a mechanical vibrating device to one of the pillars of his laboratory allegedly causing vibrations to the surrounding buildings, so he *"had to promptly remove his device to stop a catastrophe."*[14]

Around 1904 began a hard and unpredictable period for Tesla, as he ran out of money, lost his business credibility and was faced with creditors seeking the return of their financial investments. He tried to organize the sale of many of his inventions. He established a new company, "Tesla Machine Company", that produced electrical oscillators for therapeutic purposes and compressors based on mechanical oscillators. In 1908, he applied his ideas previously used with induction motors and rotating magnetic field to create bladeless turbines and pumps driven by adhesion and viscosity forces.

After the demise of his Wardenclyffe laboratory at Long Island, Tesla devoted more energy into mechanical devices such as his bladeless turbine, which he was developing for nearly ten years. He compared this turbine with an asynchronous electrical motor; its rotor consisted of a number of parallel discs attached close to each other, with just enough space between each disc to allow the steam or water to be sucked into the center exhaust. The discs would turn by means of viscosity as the fluid passes through and is released through the center. It was able to develop huge power relative to its size and weight.

However, it had shortcomings - a very high operating speed making it difficult for control, and relatively low efficiency below 50%. The initial turbines had such a small rotor it could fit into a hat and could develop up to 30 HP. The similarity between an asynchronous motor and this turbine comes from the fact that both devices tend to lose power and torque as the speed of fluid (or the rotating magnetic field) reaches the speed of the rotor.

The first turbine of this type was built by Juilus C. Czito, the son of Colman Czito Tesla's long-time machinist who worked with Tesla in Budapest, Paris, New York, and Colorado Springs. The diameter of the turbine wheel was 15cm, while the rotor consisted of eight thin discs attached close to each other having 12cm in diameter. They were fitted in a very precisely engineered housing designed to minimise the gap between the rotor and the housing. Due to extremely high speed of up to 35,000 revolutions per minute, metal discs would stretch under the centrifugal forces developed in the turbine rotor, therefore extremely precise mechanical engineering was necessary to prevent unwanted vibrations.

After meeting the wealthy industrialist J. Hedley in 1908, Tesla was awarded the contract to build the new engine for Hedley's yacht "Alabama". Next year he incorporates "The Tesla Propulsion Company" and produces several turbo machine prototypes including a pump, a compressor, a blower, a turbo-pump and finally water, steam, and gas turbines. Tesla operated from his New York office at 165 Broadway Street, accompanied by his staff consisting of several technical drafts-man and two secretaries. He spent most of his time in the office designing machines for several projects and communi-cated with the workshop engineers through letters and draw-ings. In 1909, thrilled at the possibilities based on the new mechanical principles used for his turbines, Tesla decided to submit a patent application in the U.S. and Europe, in coop-eration with the wealthy mining engineer John Hammond.

In 1910, Tesla created a new model with a 30cm wheel and at the angular velocity of 100,000 revolutions/min, which developed 100 KS, a considerably better efficiency then the first machine. He perfected this machine further by reducing

Tesla's turbopump

Tesla's bladeless turbine

the diameter and the angular velocity, which increased the efficiency and power. Encouraged by his success, he decided to make another machine and test it out on Edison Society's Waterside Power Station in New York.

Notwithstanding his genius, Tesla was a difficult person to work with, which significantly affected his life and carrier. Tesla liked to work in the afternoon and at night, which did not suit the Power Station staff because that coincided with peak load usage. In the end, Tesla made two turbines with 27.5 cm diameter wheels, which developed around 200 HP at the rotational speed of 9,000 revolutions/min. Tesla thought that they could achieve up to 600 HP by adding low-pressure units. Trying to prove this, Tesla devised a test with two turbines driven in opposite directions and measured the coupling between them while they practically stood still. It seems most people did not understand what Tesla was trying to prove with this test and consequently the project was abandonded.[14]

Looking for someone who would further help him financially, he signed a contract with Allis Chalmers from Milwaukee. Three turbines were built with pressures lower than the ones he worked with before. A considerably stronger turbine was built, with a velocity of 3,600 revolutions/min, which directly propelled the alternating current generator of 60 Hz frequency. The turbine developed around 500 kW of power and had fifteen wheels of 150 cm diameter with a separation between wheels of about 3 mm. The maximum efficiency of this machine was around 38%, with the ratio of input to output steam pressure of 80/3.

Tesla's speedometer

The research in Milwaukee did not advance as Tesla had planned; when asked why he stop working with Allis Chalmers, Tesla said that the company did not want to make a turbine the way he envisaged.

Tesla's turbines required a higher rotational velocity, which was difficult to achieve using the technology known at the time. Tesla's competitors Curtis and Parkinson had turbines that had already completed initial development phases, but Tesla did not have sufficient finances to develop his model which could potentially attract a larger investment required to turn his turbine into a commercially viable product.

Tesla develop a speedometer device by applying the results of his experimental research in the field of fluid flow between two co-rotating discs, and between a rotating disc and a stationary surface. Between 1916 and 1922, thanks to the contract with the Waltham Watch Company from Massachusetts, Tesla was able to finance his experiments and research of new measuring devices and instruments for measuring the speed of boats and the flow of fluid. In these measuring devices, Tesla used the principle of energy transfer based on fluid viscosity and its adhesive properties, the same principle he used with the turbines and pumps. Tesla received $50,000, a significant amount in those days, for the patent rights to the turbines and pumps. Tesla's invention that was protected by the patent as "Valvular Conduit" (Patent 1,329,559) in 1920 was also very interesting and original. This was a device without movable parts which acted as a nonlinear element used in the memory of pneumatic computers, thanks to which Tesla's name ended up related to this new field of technology in the sixties.

During the First World War, Tesla was vivaciously interested in the outcome. In an article from 1914, he predicted

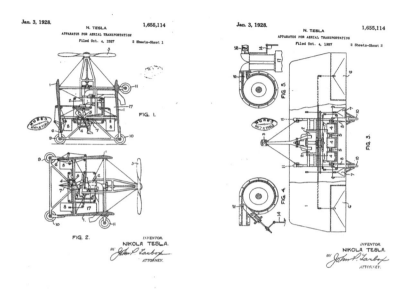

Illustrations within the patent "Apparatus for Aerial Transportation"

that it would last for four years. He based his calculations on the statistical data and his mechanical theory of life.

In an attempt to satisfy Tesla's debts, his tower at the Wardenclyffe laboratory was demolished for scrap in 1917. As the First World War was still ongoing, rumours spread among journalists that German spies were using the tower to transmit messages or as an observation post. In fact, to preserve Tesla's reputation, the real truth about the reason for demolishing the tower has not been made public. That was the end of Tesla's hopes that the project on Long Island would ever be continued. He realized that most of his ideas were way ahead of his time.

Towards the end of the 1920s, Tesla abandoned further research in the field of mechanical devices, a decision highly influenced by the Great Depression hitting U.S. economy at the time. He had to close his office but continued his work. Over the next few years he conducted research on geodynamics, death rays, and propagation of mechanical waves through the earth. He continued with attempts to attract a few large companies and even governments, including United Kingdom, Yugoslavia, and Soviet Union, with no success.

In 1928 Tesla submitted his last two patents: "The Method of Aerial Transportation"(Patent 1,655,113) and "Device for Aerial Transportation" (Patent 1,655,114). According to Tesla: "The invention consists of a new type of flying machine, designated helicopterplane, which may be raised and lowered vertically and driven horizontally by the same propelling devices" .[61] It may be surprising to see Tesla suddenly working on aviation topics, however, his life-long interest in aerodynamics, precision mechanical devices, turbines and propelling motors somehow came together in his mature years.

VII

AWARDS AND
RECOGNITIONS

During his lifetime Nikola Tesla received a large number of honorary doctorates from some of the most renowned universities in the world, and even more medals and distinction awards honoring his fascinating contribution to the world of science. He started receiving such acknowledgments towards the end of the nineteenth century, following a number of lectures in America and Europe, which raised his status in the world of science. In 1893, he received the "Elliot Cresson" gold medal from the Franklin Institute for research in the field of high frequency currents. The following year, he was elected as a corresponding member of the Serbian Royal Academy, received his first honorable doctorate from Columbia University, and later from the University of Yale. In 1895 he became a regular member of the American Society for Advancement of Science, in 1896 a member of the American Electro Therapeutic Society, in 1907 a member of the New York Academy of Science, and in 1908 he received the honorable doctorate of the High Technical School in Vienna. During 1917, two significant acknowledgments came his way: he became the first chosen member of the highest rank of the American Institute of Electrical Engineers and received the Edison gold medal award from the same institution. At the award ceremony, the president of the commission for the Edison medal, B.A. Behrend, one of the first electrical engineers who understood the greatness of Tesla's polyphase system and induction motor, said:[62]

"By an extraordinary coincidence, it is exactly 29 years ago, to the very day and hour, that there stood before this Institute Nikola Tesla. Not since the appearance of Faraday's ex-

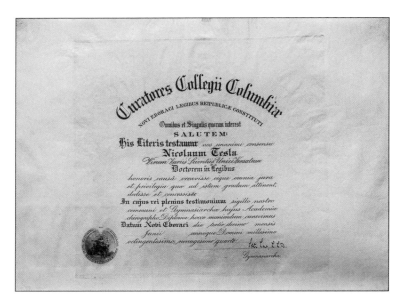

Diploma of the Honorary PhD from Columbia College

perimental researches in electricity has a great experimental truth been voiced so simply and so clearly as this description of Mr. Tesla's great discovery of the generation and utilization of polyphase alternating currents. He left nothing to be done for those who followed him. His paper contained the skeleton even of the mathematical theory.

Three years later, in 1891, there was given the first great demonstration, by Swiss engineers, of the transmission of power at 30,000 volts from Lauffen to Frankfort by means of Mr. Tesla's system. A few years later this was followed by the development of the Cataract Construction Company, under the presidency of our member, Edward A. Adams, and with the aid of the engineers of the Westinghouse Company. It is interesting to recall here tonight that in Lord Kelvin's report to Mr. Adams, Lord Kelvin recommended the use of direct current for the development of power at Niagara Falls and for its transmission to Buffalo.

The due appreciation or even enumeration of the results of Mr. Tesla's invention is neither practicable nor desirable at this moment. There is a time for all things. Suffice it to say that, were we to seize and to eliminate from our industrial world the results of Mr. Tesla's work, the wheels of industry would cease to turn, our electric cars and trains would stop, our towns would be dark, our mills would be dead and idle. Yea, so far-reaching is this work that it has become the warp and woof of industry.

The due appreciation or even enumeration of the results of Mr. Tesla's invention is neither practicable nor desirable at this moment. There is a time for all things. Suffice it to say that, were we to seize and to eliminate from our industrial world the results of Mr. Tesla's work, the wheels of industry would cease to turn, our electric cars and trains would stop, our towns would be dark, our mills would be dead and idle. Yea, so far reaching is this work, that it has become the warp and woof of industry.

HIS name marks an epoch in the advance of electrical science. From THAT work has sprung a revolution in the electrical art.

We asked Mr. Tesla to accept this medal. We did not do this for the mere sake of conferring a distinction, or of perpetuating a name; for so long as men occupy themselves with our industry, his work will be incorporated in the common thought of our art, and the name of Tesla runs no more risk of oblivion than does that of Faraday, or that of Edison. Nor indeed does

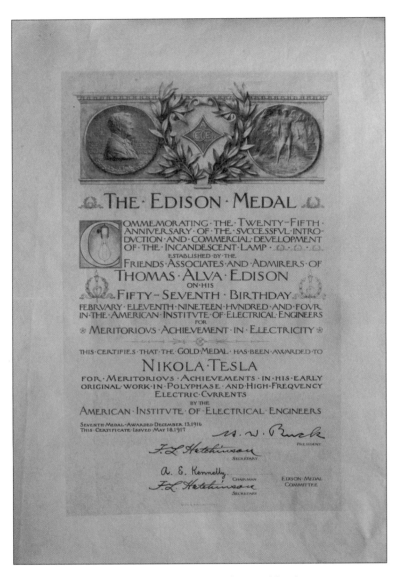

Edison Gold Medal award, issued by the
American Institute of Electrical Engineers

this Institute give this medal as evidence that Mr. Tesla's work has received its official sanction. His work stands in no need of such sanction.

No, Mr. Tesla, we beg you to cherish this medal as a symbol of our gratitude for the new creative thought, the powerful impetus, akin to revolution, which you have given to our art and to our science. You have lived to see the work of your genius established. What shall a man desire more than this? There rings out to us a paraphrase of Pope's lines on Newton: Nature and Nature's laws lay hid in night God said, 'Let Tesla be,' and all was light."

Tesla was awarded the Edison medal thirty years after his invention of the polyphase system; many people who attended the ceremony were not aware of the past animosity between Tesla and Edison, and their battles between direct and alternative current systems. According to some biographies, Behrend had to persuade Tesla to accept this award.

In honor of his seventieth birthday in 1926, Tesla received the honorable doctorate from the Universities of Belgrade and Zagreb, in 1933 became a member of the National Geographic Association of America, and in 1934 received the "John Scott" medal from the city of Philadelphia for his work on the rotating magnetic field and induction motor.

Five years later, for his seventy-fifth birthday, Tesla was presented a book with original congratulation letters from prominent scientists who, with great respect, remembered his great merits for the development of civilization.

After the celebration of his eightieth birthday, which was organized in many cities in Europe, Tesla received a series of distinguished doctorates: 1936, higher technical school in Prague; 1937, higher technical school in Graz and Brno, Universities in Poitiers and Paris, Poly-technical school in Bucharest. The same year he was chosen as a regular member of the Serbian Royal Academy of Science. In 1938, he received the honorary doctorate from the Grenoble University, and the following year his last acknowledgment, the honorary doctorate from the Sofia University. Over the course of his life, Tesla was awarded a number of state orders from Serbian, Montenegrian, and Czech governments such as the Order of St. Sava second degree, Prince Danilo, the White Lion and others.

VIII

NIKOLA TESLA
BIOGRAPHY

Before he published his autobiography with an interesting title, "My Inventions,"[5] Tesla was widely known as a remarkable, creative human being, deeply committed to the research of unveiling the secrets of electricity, but his personal life was a mystery. As soon as it was published in 1919, Tesla's autobiography provoked a lot of interest; its title came from Tesla's belief that his inventions were "his life" and that everything else was subordinated to them. He searched for the source of his inventions in his early years and consequently gave particular attention to his childhood experiences and beliefs.

While writing the story of his life, he thought about young people in particular, showing them the roots of success in life, and how to take opportunity of inventive thoughts that may emerge early in their lives. Naturally, Tesla's messages are typical of advice given by elders to the younger generation, but they carry significantly more weight as they come from a creator who made a huge life achievement by fighting endlessly for his ideas. His example shows that everyone will have obstacles to overcome, no matter how right he is or how worth his offering to humanity is. Each person's life achievements are bound by their ability and determination; some will reach the universe, while others live day by day. Tesla had to overcome a huge number of problems, but he was driven by a massive inner energy fueled with his creative intellect and self-belief with a noble aim to enhance human wellbeing by understanding the laws of nature and applying them to human benefit. He left us a hugely valuable legacy of applied inventions that changed the face of earth, as well as many grand ideas, that are yet to be fully understood. He remains a fascinating and somewhat mysterious scientist, inventor, and person even today, more than a hundred years after conceiving his greatest inventions which are surrounding us ubiquitously.

Tesla's autobiography is exceptionally interesting and valuable as it presents previously unknown facts about Tesla's views of the world, his feelings, reasoning, relationship towards science, and problems of the society. In his childhood Tesla used to astound his neighborhood by witty mischiefs, which according to Tesla, contained hints of his future ideas and inventions; in his mature years he continued to astound the world with his inventions and thoughts in science and technology.

The first two chapters Tesla devotes to his childhood and early inventions that shaped his mind and character. In subsequent chapters, he writes about his most important inventions: the rotating magnetic field, Tesla coil, and the high frequency transformer. He devoted an entire chapter to his high frequency and high voltage "magnifying transmitter" built on Long Island, explaining in detail his vision of what his "World System" could enable. At the end of this chapter he wrote: *My project was retarded by laws of nature. The world was not prepared for it. It was too far ahead of time. But the same laws will prevail in the end and make it a triumphal success.*

Tesla has put so much effort into his high frequency magnifying transmitter, so he returns to this topic in the next chapter dedicated to teleautomatics:

"The terrible conflict is still uppermost in the minds and perhaps the greatest importance will be attached to the Mag-

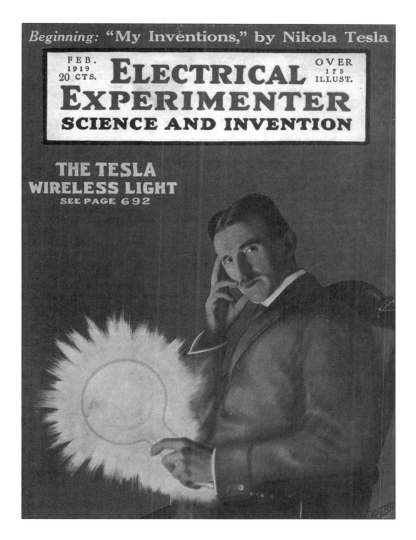

Front page of the "Electrical Experimenter" magazine,
which published Tesla's autobiography in six sequels

An Illustration of the imagined final look of Tesla's Tower at Long Island, published in the "Electrical Experimenter" magazine on 18th June 1919.

nifying Transmitter as a machine for attack and defense, more particularly in connection with Telautomatics. This invention is a logical outcome of observations begun in my boyhood and continued thruout my life. When the first results were publisht the Electrical Review stated editorially that it would become one of the "most potent factors in the advance and civilization of mankind." The time is not distant when this prediction will be fulfilled. In 1898 and 1900 it was offered to the Government and might have been adopted were I one of those who would go to Alexander's shepherd when they want a favor from Alexander. At that time I really thought that it would abolish war, because of its unlimited destructiveness and exclusion of the personal element of combat. But while I have not lost faith in its potentialities, my views have changed since.

War can not be avoided until the physical cause for its recurrence is removed and this, in the last analysis, is the vast extent of the planet on which we live. Only thru annihilation of distance in every respect, as the conveyance of intelligence, transport of passengers and supplies and transmission of energy will conditions be brought about some day, insuring permanency of friendly relations. What we now want most is closer contact and better understanding between individuals and communities all over the earth, and the elimination of that fanatic devotion to exalted ideals of national egoism and pride which is always prone to plunge the world into primeval barbarism and strife. No league or parliamentary act of any kind will ever prevent such a calamity. These are only new devices for putting the weak at the mercy of the strong. I have exprest myself in this regard fourteen years ago, when a combination of a few leading governments - a sort of Holy Alliance - was advocated by the late Andrew Carnegie, who may be fairly con-

sidered as the father of this idea, having given to it more publicity and impetus than anybody else prior to the efforts of the President. While it can not be denied that such a pact might be of material advantage to some less fortunate peoples, it can not attain the chief object sought. Peace can only come as a natural consequence of universal enlightenment and merging of races, and we are still far from this blissful realization."

Tesla wrote "My Inventions" in 1919, around 14 years after his greatest and most famous inventions and projects. Had he written this book in his peak, when he was a celebrity, it could have made a much stronger impact, however, at that time Tesla was still completely devoted to research. The publisher of the "Electrical Experimenter" magazine, Hugo Gernsback, tried for nearly ten years to convince Tesla to write for his magazine. He even offered Tesla a partnership which he believed would have raised the profile of the magazine. Gernsback collaborated with Tesla, "a visionary and inventor without boundaries", who was known for his extravagant statements to the press.

In his late years, Tesla started being increasingly inward looking and detached from reality. His unusual and provocative statements gave way for many opportunists and fanatics to start reshaping his actual role in science and technology. Tesla's gradual decline from reality increased in the years he was left without his laboratories where his experiments would "bring him back" from the imaginary world into reality; he had a fascinating mind and imagination but really excelled when he could turn his thoughts into real artefacts. This was obvious even in the days when he was writing his autobiography, but it was demonstrated more and more in the years after 1919.

IX

CONCLUDING WORDS

Nikola Tesla was a scientist who dedicated his entire life to answering the secrets of nature and applying them to the benefit of humankind. Born to a Serbian family in a small village in the Balkans, he managed to become a famed 'citizen of the world' in his early thirties, but never forgot his origins and his old homeland which he continued to help throughout his life, to the extent possible. He was a deeply humane person, who made a huge contribution to our civilisation with his fascinating inventions and unselfish love towards the entire mankind. He wasn't searching for wealth or fame; his aims were far bigger; he was a visionary who left behind a bewildering legacy of successfully applied inventions as well as thoughts for the future. He received numerous acknowledgments from the world's most respected scientific institutions and was listed in the Hall of Fame in the United States. As one of the biggest recognitions a scientist can have, the unit of magnetic induction was named "tesla" after him.

Patents played a critical role in Tesla's research work. He would always submit the patent application for his new inventions before providing information to the public. His first patents explained inventions related to arc illumination and generation of direct current, because at the time he wasn't yet ready to apply for the patents in the field of induction motors and polyphase currents systems. He managed to sell patent rights to his first few patents and used the proceeds to fund his research and experimentation with machines and motors for alternating currents. His subsequent patents on polyphase system generation, transmission and utilization of alternat-

Nikola Tesla in his office in New York, around 1910

ing currents caused a real revolution in electrical engineering. He sold these patent rights to the Westinghouse Company in order to invest in a new laboratory and further research in the field of high frequency currents. This research generated a whole new series of patents, including alternating high frequency generators, Tesla's transformer, and the system of high frequency alternating current transmission with the use of open (antenna, ground, coil) and closed resonant circuits. After the demise of his 'World Station' laboratory at Long Island in 1905, he moved on to patent a range of innovations related to mechanical devices, such as turbines, pumps, speedometers, frequency measuring devices, fluid flow meters, etc. His last two patents described the lightning conductor and vertical take-off planes. During the period between May 1885 to October 1927, Tesla had 111 US patents. The correct number of patents applied abroad has not yet been confirmed, but it is estimated to over 167. Most foreign patents are replicas from the American patents. According to the latest findings, Tesla has 116 original patents from which 109 are US and 7 British. The list of inventions that are protected by these patents stands at 125. For his inventions in 26 countries, Tesla was awarded a total of 278 patents, and possibly more.

Tesla with the Westinghouse company representatives, 10th May 1938 in New York, celebrating 50th anniversary of Tesla's induction motor invention. The illustrated motor was made by the Westinghouse company in Pittsburgh as a lookalike of the first induction motor constructed by Tesla in Strasbourg in 1883.

Nikola Tesla, for whom many wrote that he could have been the wealthiest man in the world if he only wanted to, spent many of his years in poverty. In the latter years of his life he could not afford to have a laboratory, but he kept a small number of his instruments which he occasionally used. A small amount of his belongings were found in storage, which Tesla's inheritor, Sava Kosanović, gathered up from a number of New York warehouses and sent to Belgrade after Tesla's death on January 7, 1943. Today, Tesla's instruments and his urn are kept in the Museum of Nikola Tesla in Belgrade, which was inaugurated in 1952.

Tesla's life and work was celebrated at conferences and gatherings organized in 1936, 1956, 1991 and 1996 in Yugoslavia, and 2006 in Serbia devoted to the 150th anniversary of his birth; smaller gatherings were held in Vienna and some other cities in Europe. Tesla was invited to the 1936 celebration, but he could not attend due to old age. Soon after, the Nikola Tesla Society has been formed and inaugurated the Nikola Tesla Institute in Belgrade; it continues to spread scientific knowledge to this day. One hundredth anniversary of Nikola Tesla's birth was officially celebrated in 1956, coinciding with the first birthday of the "Nikola Tesla Museum" in Belgrade. In the same year, the international Technical Committee of the International Electrotechnical Commission and the International Committee for Weights and Measures announced its decision that the unit of magnetic induction is to be named "tesla." In 1975, the Institute of Electrical and Electronic Engineers established the "Nikola Tesla" award for *Outstanding contributions to the generation and utilization of electric power*". The "Nikola Tesla" foundation, which was established in 1979 by the Nikola Tesla Society, presented awards to distinguished scientists, experts, researchers and young researchers for their contribution in science and engineering. Nikola Tesla Memorial Society based in New York has a large group of members and was active on the popularization of Nikola Tesla's works through newspaper articles, movies, and Internet sites. Another organization promoting Tesla's work was the "International Tesla Society", headquartered in Colorado Springs, active between 1984 and 1998. They organized symposiums, published books on Tesla, and had a museum featuring photos of Tesla's laboratories, many interesting research devices, and a laboratory full of fascinating electrical and mechanical devices.

REFERENCES

[1] Opšta enciklopedija LAROUSSE, Tom 3: Istorija, Vuk Karadžić, Beograd, 1973.

[2] Грант К. Цверава: „Никола Тесла (1856–1943)", Клуб НТ, Београд, 2006.

[3] Marc Seifer: "Wizard – The Life and Times of Nikola Tesla", New York, Citadel Press, 1998.

[4] Enciklopedija Jugoslavije, izdanje Leksikografskog zavoda, Zagreb, knjiga 4.

[5] Никола Тесла: "Моји изуми", Клуб НТ, Београд, 2006.

[6] F. Pichler: "On the University Studies of Nikola Tesla in Graz and Prague", Proc. of the XVII European Meeting on Cybernetics and System Research, Vienna, 13–16 April 2004, pp. 803–807.

[7] Никола Тесла: "О капиларним цевима", Србадија, Алманах за 1884. годину, Нови Сад.

[8] Божидар Ковачек: "Никола Тесла и Матица српска", Матица српска, 2006.

[9] Славко Бокшан: "Никола Тесла и његово дело", Клуб НТ, Београд, 2006.

[10] Aleksandar Damjanović: "Contribution a l'Histoire de l'Electrotechnique", Bulletin de l'Association Suisse des Elektriciens, No. 20, Zurich, Oct. 1960.

[11] Коста Кулишић: "Никола Тесла – његов студентски живот и научни рад", Сарајево, 1936.

[12] Robert Friedel & Paul Israel: "Edison's Electric Light", Rutgers University Press, New Brunswick, New Jersey, 1986.

[13] Nikola Tesla: "A New System of Alternate Current Motors and Transformers", lecture delivered before the AIEE, May 16, 1888.

[14] Џон О'Нил: "Ненадмашни геније", А–Ш дело, Земун, Београд, 1993.

[15] Margaret Cheney: "Tesla – Man Out of Time", Englewood Cliffs, 1981.

[16] Professor Anthony: "Discussion", after Tesla's lecture [13].

[17] (Петар Мандић?): "СРПСКИ ЕДИСОН (Никола Тесла)", Браник, бр. 135, год. V, 16. новембра 1889, Нови Сад.

[18] видети [14].

[19] Nikola Tesla: "Experiments with alternate currents of very high frequency and their application to methods of artificial illumination", lecture delivered before A.I.E.E., at Columbia College, May 20, 1891 republished many times after publication in *Electrical Engineer,* New York, July 8, 1891, pp. 25–48.

[20] Nikola Tesla: "System of electric lighting", U.S. patent, 454,622, June 23, 1891. Applied April 25, 1891.

[21] A. Oberbeck: "Ueber der Verlauf der Elektrischen Schwingungen bei den Tesla'schen Versuchen", Wied. Ann. Der Physik, 1895, vol. 55, s. 623.

[22] Зорица Циврић, Братислав Стојиљковић: "Никола Тесла у Београду 1892", Музеј Николе Тесле, Београд, 2002.

[23] Дубравка Смиљанић, Зорица Циврић: "Никола Тесла – Преписка с родбином", Музеј Николе Тесле, Београд, 1993.

[24] Србобран, 23. маја (4. јуна) 1892.

[25] Србобран, 30. маја (11. јуна) 1892.

[26] Thomas C. Martin: "The Inventions, Researches and Writings of Nikola Tesla", New York, 1894.

[27] Robert Underwood Johnson: Selected songs of Zmaj Jovan Jovanović, translated by Nikola Tesla.

[28] Nikola Tesla: "On Light and other High Frequency Phenomena", lecture before the Franklin Institute, Philadelphia, Feb. 1893, and before the National Electric Light Association, St. Louis, March 1893.

[29] Никола Тесла, слајд, Музеј Николе Тесле, Београд.

[30] M. Lemme and R. Menicucci: "From the coherer to DSP", EBU Technical Review, No. 263, Spring 1995.

[31] World's Fair, Chicago 1893.

[32] The Art of Electric Power Development and Transmission 1890–1893, Chapter XXI Niagara Power – History of the Niagara Falls Power Company 1886–1918, Vol. II, Niagara Falls, NY 1927.

[33] Славко Бокшан: "Никола Тесла и његов пионирски рад у електротехници", А–Ш дело, Београд, 1993.

[34] Niagara Power – History of the Niagara Falls Power Company 1886–1918, Vol. II, Niagara Falls, NY 1927.

[35] S. E. Brown: Letter to "Electrical World", Nov. 7, 1891.

[36] The Tesla Patent: Sweeping Decision in Favor of These Patents by the U.S. Circuit Court, "Electrical Review", N.Y., 19. IX 1900, p. 288.

[37] Charles F. Scott: "Tesla's Contribution to Electric Power", Electrical Engineering, August 1943.

[38] Nikola Tesla: "On Electricity", the address on the occasion of the commemoration of the introduction of Niagara Falls power in Buffalo at the Elliot Club, January 12, 1897.

[39] видети [14].

[40] Nikola Tesla: "On Roentgen Rays", Electrical Review, March 11, 1896.

[41] Nikola Tesla: Lecture before New York Academy of Science, April 6, 1897, Завод за уџбенике и наставна средства, Београд.

[42] Guglielmo Marconi: British Pat. No. 12,039 of 1896.

[43] Guglielmo Marconi: "Improvements in Apparatus for Wireless Telegraphy", British Pat. No. 7777, accepted 13th Apr., 1901, applied, 26th Apr., 1900.

[44] Guglielmo Marconi: "Apparatus for Wireless Telegraphy", American Pat. No. 763,772, patented June 28, 1904. Applied Nov. 10, 1900.

[45] "Marconi Wireless Telegraph Company of America v. United States", Case adjudged in the Supreme Court of the United States at October term, 1942.

[46] Nikola Tesla: "Method of and Apparatus for Controlling Mechanism of Moving Vessels", Pat. No. 613,809, Nov. 8, 1898. Applied July 1, 1898.

[47] Nikola Tesla: "The problem of increasing human energy", Century Illustrated Monthly Magazine, June 1900.

[48] Nikola Tesla: "Colorado Springs Notes 1899–1900", Nolit, Belgrade, 1978.

[49] Nikola Tesla: "System of Transmission of Electrical Energy", Pat. No. 645,576, March 1900. Application filed September 2, 1897.

[50] Nikola Tesla: "Electrical Transformer", Pat. No. 593,138, Nov. 2, 1897. Application filed March 20, 1897.

[51] Nikola Tesla: "Long Island Notes", Archive of Nikola Tesla Museum, Belgrade.

[52] Nikola Tesla: "Art of Transmitting Electrical Energy Through the Natural Mediums", Pat. No. 787,412, April 18, 1905. Application filed May 16, 1900.

[53] Leland Anderson, ed.: "Nikola Tesla on his work with alternating currents and their application to wireless telegraphy and telephony and transmission of power", Sun Publishing, Denver, 1992.

[54] Tapan K. Sarkar, R. J. Mailoux, A. A. Oliner, M. Salazar-Palma, D. L. Sengupta: "History of Wireless", John Wiley and Sons, Inc., 2006.

[55] Nikola Tesla: "Colorado Springs Notes", издање на енглеском језику с коментарима А. Маринчића, Завод за уџбенике и наставна средства, Београд, 2005.

[56] K. L. Corum, J. F. Corum and A. H. Aidinejad: "Atmospheric Fields, Tesla's Receivers and Regenerative Detectors", Proc. of the 1994 International Tesla Symposium, Colorado Springs, Colorado.

[57] J. F. Corum and K. L. Corum: "The application of transmission line resonators to high voltage power proceedings: history, analysis and experiment", 19th Southern Symposium on System Theory, March 15–17, 1987, Clemson.

[58] J. R. Wait: "Historical background and introduction to special issue on extremely low frequency (ELF) propagation", IEEE Trans. on Com., COM–22, No. 4, April 1974.

[59] Nikola Tesla: "Method of Intensifying and Utilizing Effects Transmitted through Natural Media", Pat. No. 685,953, Nov. 5, 1901. Application filed June 24, 1899.

[60] Nikola Tesla: "System of Signaling", Pat. No. 725,605, Apr. 14, 1903. Application filed July 16, 1900.

[61] Nikola Tesla: "Apparatus for Aerial Transportation", Pat. No. 1,655,114, Jan. 3, 1928. Application filed October 4, 1927.

[62] Nikola Tesla receives Edison Medal: Address by Bernard A. Behrend, Electrical Review and Western Electrician, New York, Vol. 70, May 26, 1917.

ABOUT THE AUTHOR

Academician Aleksandar Marinčić (1933-2011), a man of remarkable and versatile interests and an impressive scientific career, possessed an innate curiosity that fuelled his extraordinary research spirit and aspiration to understand the secrets of nature. He devoted his life to science, and in particular to the dissemination of knowledge about the fascinating creative paths of great people, most notably scientists and inventors, Nikola Tesla and Mihajlo Pupin. He is the initiator of many important projects related to the preservation and affirmation of Tesla's and Pupin's heritage.

Professor Marinčić obtained his PhD at the University of Sheffield (England) in 1963 and started his rich scientific career at the Faculty of Electrical Engineering, University of Belgrade in 1958. Between 1967 and 1971, he held the position of UNESCO expert, Visiting Associate Professor and Acting Chief Technical Adviser at the Middle-East Technical University in Ankara, Turkey. Following his return to Belgrade, he rejoined the Faculty of Electrical Engineering, where he has been a full professor since 1980, and held positions of Vice-Dean and Head of Telecommunications Department. He had also lectured at the Faculty of Electronic Engineering in Nis and the Faculty of Technical Sciences in Novi Sad, and had given guest lectures across universities and conferences in England, Wales, the United States, Austria, Turkey and the countries of the former Yugoslavia. Professor Marinčić was elected a corresponding member of the Serbian Academy of Sciences and Arts in April 1991, and a full-time member in October 2000.

Aleksandar Marinčić has devoted a significant part of his remarkable career to Nikola Tesla, who fascinated him from the student days, and inspired him to understand the achievements and ways of thinking of such a genius engineer and inventor. "I guess that's where I got my persistence and interest in work," he wrote in his memoirs.

He was the second director of the Nikola Tesla Museum in Belgrade for 14 years, from 1982 to 1996, however, his close relation with this institution goes back to his student days. When the Museum was just opened to the public in 1955, he was among the first students of the Faculty of Electrical Engineering who were invited as demonstrators of Tesla's inventions on the permanent display in the Museum. Shortly afterwards, Aleksandar left for England, gained his PhD and returned to Belgrade, where his affiliation with the museum and knowledge of Tesla's legacy, earned him an advisory role.

In his own words, he learned a lot from the first director of the Museum and one of its key founders, Professor Veljko Korać: " Admittedly, I've learned a lot from Korać, and he has helped me see Tesla beyond a 'pure' electrical engineer. Through conversations with him, I realised that I should correct my perceptions of Tesla, and not only recognise him as a brilliant and ingenious engineer, but a man who approached nature and problems in a different way, far more ambitiously and holistically than even the most talented engineer would."

Professor Marinčić initiated a number of new activities at the museum, most notably the publication of Tesla's diaries and lesser known works, which were at the time available only to a handful of people who had access to the museum's documentation archive. One of the most significant books authored by Professor Marinčić was the famous diary of research notes written by Nikola Tesla during his stay at Colorado Springs, published in 1976 in Serbian and two years later in

English. He spent two years working on this publication that was eagerly awaited by the entire scientific and professional world. The insightful comments he wrote to complement and explain Tesla's research notes were one of its greatest assets. Professor Marinčić possessed a vast knowledge not only of Tesla's work, but of all the contributions made by scientists and researchers who took part in the creation of Tesla's most valuable inventions. He was an inspirational guide, who had such a deep expertise and knowledge, that he was able to give simple explanations to complex problems, guiding curious readers through Tesla's experiments and complex thought pathways that created some of the greatest inventions in the field of electrical engineering.

In addition to the executive roles at the University of Belgrade and the Nikola Tesla Museum, Professor Marinčić was president of the Nikola Tesla Society for the promotion of scientific knowledge, and since 2000, the President of the Tesla Memorial Society in New York. He organised and participated in numerous international congresses, symposia, and other scientific and professional gatherings dedicated to Tesla. He participated in a number of television shows dedicated to Tesla, bearing in mind the significance of media in disseminating the importance and true appreciation of Tesla's work. His last public appearance, when he reflected with deep emotions on how the life-long research of Tesla's life brought fulfilment to his own life, was recorded at the Nikola Tesla museum in Belgrade and aired on Radio Television of Serbia in September 2010, along with the famous 1982 BBC documentary, "The Mysterious Mr. Tesla", featuring Professor Marinčić as the newly appointed director of the Nikola Tesla Museum.

Following many scientific, professional, and popular articles, editorials, commentaries and reviews that he published during his study of Nikola Tesla's work for more than five decades, Professor Marinčić accepted with great pleasure to be the scientific reviewer of a new book to be published by the Nikola Tesla Museum, "The Unfulfilled Patents of Nikola Tesla - inventions that Tesla did not protect." In this book, published in 2010, previously unpublished material from Tesla's personal legacy was shared publicly for the first time. At the same time, Professor Marinčić accepted, with the utmost enthusiasm, the task of selecting and processing various archival materials with over 1500 sheets of preserved notes written by Nikola Tesla at Long Island. In a very short period of time, he had successfully interpreted, digitised, and prepared for print several hundred hard-to-read drawings and schematics. Serious illness prevented him from completing this work. Sadly, we will never be able to read his precious expert comments from this period of Tesla's life and work to which he, with almost youthful enthusiasm, wanted to return and interpret it with his accumulated experience and the wisdom of an experienced scientist and researcher.

Just as the world will wait a long time for another genius such as Nikola Tesla, we will forever miss Aleksandar Marinčić, an extraordinary insider and expert of Tesla's work. One of his final legacies, the book you are reading, "Nikola Tesla - The Life and Inventions of a Genius", had become even more precious. The man who made a huge contribution to the popularization, understanding and true appreciation of Tesla's work, in this book accomplished his long-standing efforts to, as he put it, "make Tesla more accessible and popular within the world of science on the planet."

Vladimir Jelenković,
Director of The Nikola Tesla Museum 2006 - 2014